# THE USBORNE SCIENCE QUIZBOOK

**Paul Dowswell and Marit Claridge**

Edited by Judy Tatchell and Lisa Miles

Designed by Ruth Russell and Fiona Brown

Illustrated by Chris Lyon and Chris Shields

Additional text by Carol Varley

Consultants: Peter McKerchar, Geoffrey Puplett, John and Margaret Rostron

## Contents



## About this book

This book is an introduction to scientific ideas. It looks at what things are made of and how they work – from plants and animals, to racing cars and video cameras. The book also explains natural forces and effects, such as gravity, electricity, sound and light.

## How to do the quizzes

Throughout the book there are quiz questions to answer as you go along, printed in italic type, *like this.* Some of the questions rely on your general knowledge, others have clues elsewhere on the page. Keep a note of your answers and check them against the answers on pages 28-31.

## The Megaquiz

On pages 26-27 is the Megaquiz – a set of ten quick quizzes to test you on your general knowledge and what you have read about in this book.

# Exploring space

**The whole of space and everything in it is known as the Universe. Scientists do not know how large the Universe is, but the part they do know about contains millions of groups of stars, called galaxies. Each galaxy is in turn made up of millions of stars.**

## Where is the Earth?

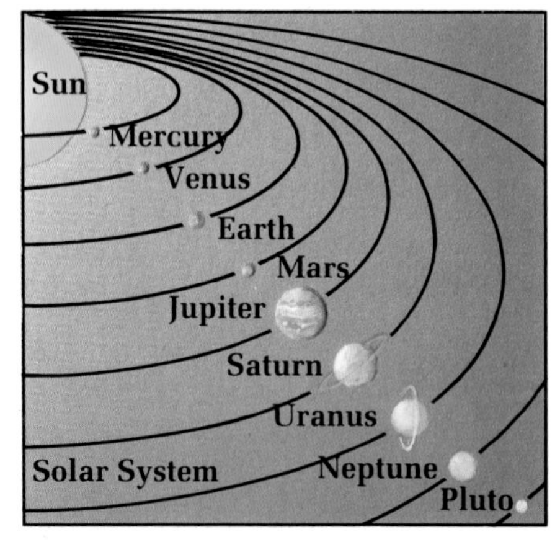


The Earth is one of nine planets which circle around a central star, the Sun. The Sun and its planets are called a solar system. The Sun is a star in the galaxy called the Milky Way.

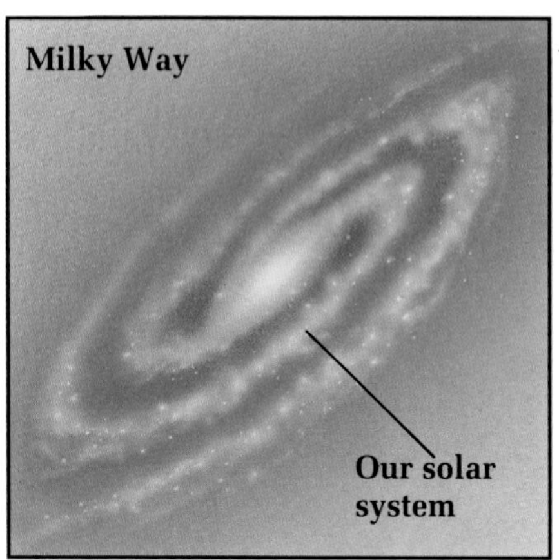


As far as we know, the Earth is the only planet that provides the air, water and warmth that living things need. It is just the right distance away from the Sun for water to exist as a liquid, rather than gas or ice. Earth's atmosphere also protects it from getting too hot or too cold.

*1. Venus, Neptune and Mars are named after: a) Roman gods; b) astronomers; c) Egyptian pharaohs.*

*2. Are Sirius, Betelgeuse and Alpha Centauri stars or planets?*

## How old is the Universe?

Most scientists believe that the Universe began about 15 thousand million years ago. An enormous explosion, called the Big Bang, created an immensely hot, dense fireball. Everything in the Universe came from this fireball. The force of this explosion was so great that stars and galaxies are still being blasted away from each other, and the Universe is still expanding.

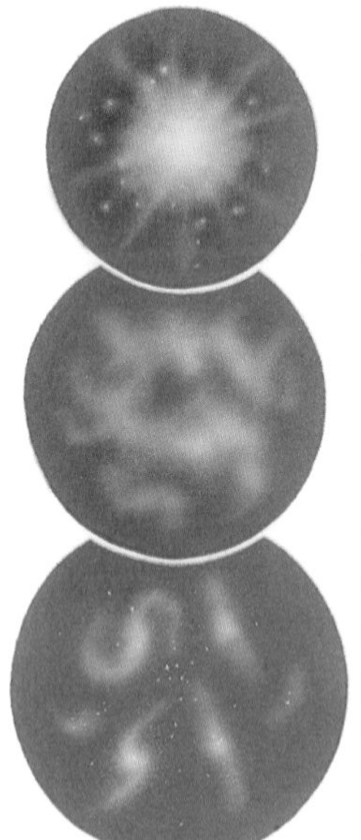

**The fireball was made of hydrogen gas.**

**The gas formed a dense cloud of particles which broke into separate clouds.**

**These clouds became galaxies of stars, like our own Milky Way.**

## How do we know what is in space?

Scientists use a variety of telescopes to see what is out in space. For example, optical telescopes use lenses to magnify light. These telescopes were first used about 400 years ago and enabled astronomers to get a closer look at the night sky. Today, photographic film and electronic sensors can record faint images that the eye cannot see.

Stars and planets give off other rays besides the light we can see. Telescopes can now detect radio waves, ultra-violet and X-ray signals from stars which are so distant they cannot be seen by even the most powerful optical telescopes.

**This radio telescope picks up radio waves from stars which cannot be seen by optical telescopes.**

*3. Radio waves from stars contain: a) blips, bleeps and hisses; b) alien traffic reports; c) light music.*

*4. Einstein was the first scientist to use a telescope. True or false?*

## Why is the Sun hot?

The Sun is an immense ball of burning hydrogen gas. It releases huge amounts of energy in a similar way to a nuclear bomb, in the form of heat and light. The Sun is so big, it is taking millions of years to burn.

**The temperature at the surface is about 6,000°C (11,000°F).**

**Sun**

**The middle of the Sun is 2,500 times hotter than the surface.**

*7. One day the Sun will go out. True or false?*

*8. Is it safe to look directly at the Sun?*

*9. Which one of these would you find in space: a) a purple pixie; b) a white dwarf; c) a green gremlin?*

*5. You can see X-rays and ultra-violet rays. True or false?*

*6. A group of stars is called: a) a compound; b) a collection; c) a constellation.*

## How does a rocket fly?

Rockets need an immense amount of energy to blast themselves out of the Earth's atmosphere. They burn fuel, which creates hot gas which escapes through exhaust nozzles. This produces a force like air rushing out of the end of a balloon, which pushes the rocket forwards.

The space shuttle uses two sets of rockets to blast it into space. Once in space, launch rockets and the main fuel tank fall back to Earth.

The shuttle can launch satellites in space, or carry out scientific experiments. It glides back to Earth and lands like an aircraft.

*10. The first spacecraft to land men on the Moon was called: a) Sputnik; b) Apollo 11; c) Starship Enterprise.*

*11. Dogs have been up in space. True or false?*

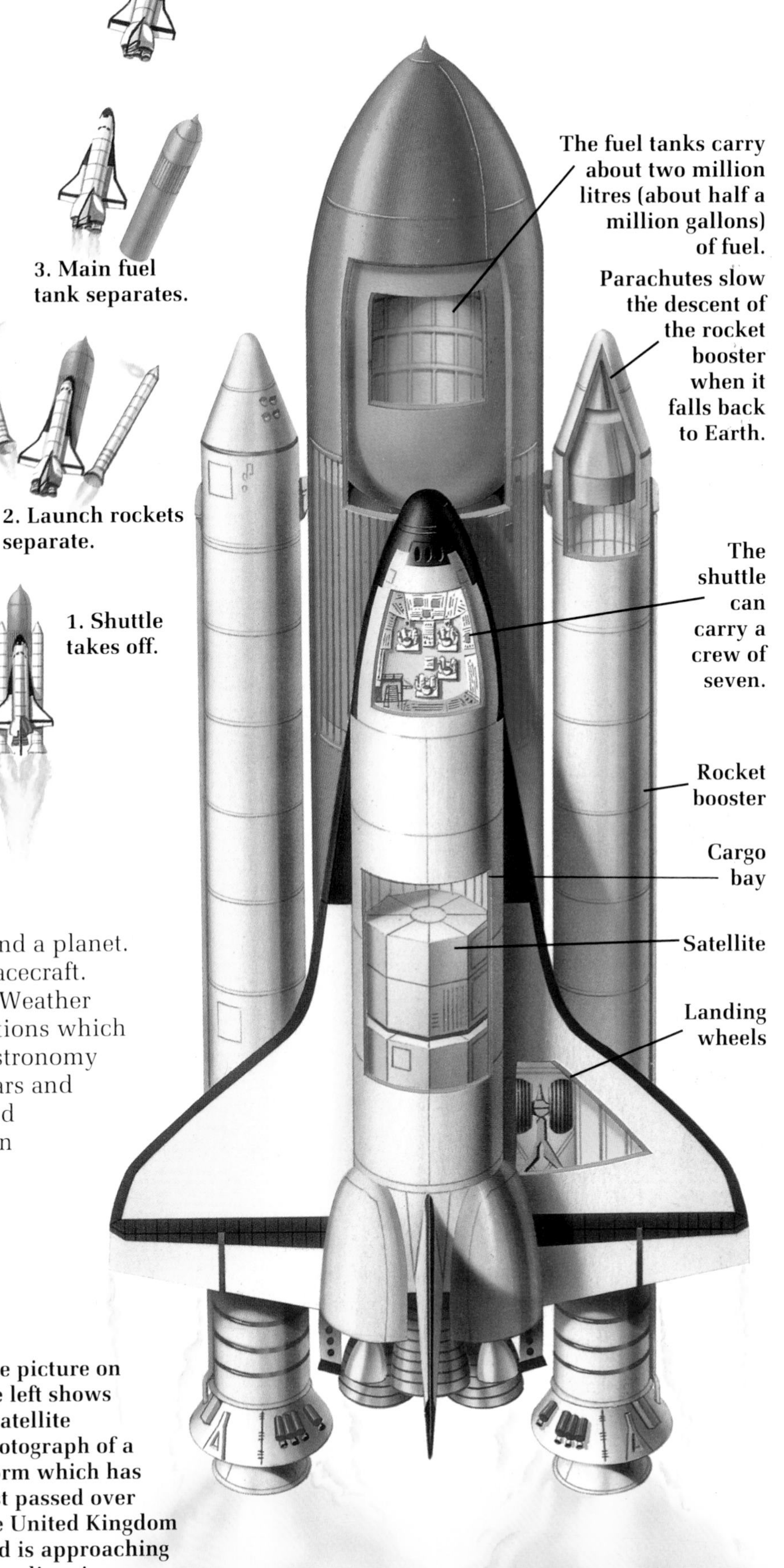


## What is a satellite?

A satellite is anything that orbits around a planet. The Moon is a satellite, and so is a spacecraft. Man-made satellites have many uses. Weather satellites take pictures of cloud formations which can be used to predict the weather. Astronomy satellites send back information on stars and planets. Communication satellites send telephone conversations and television transmissions around the world.

**The picture on the left shows a satellite photograph of a storm which has just passed over the United Kingdom and is approaching Scandinavia.**

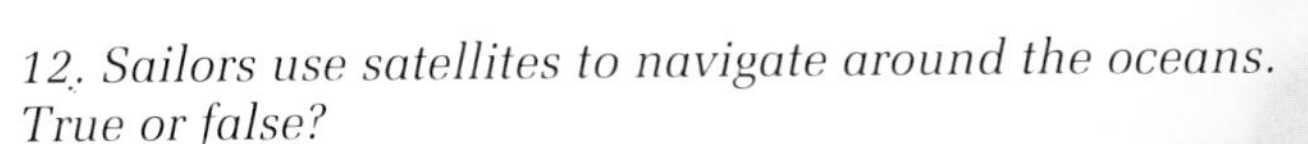

*12. Sailors use satellites to navigate around the oceans. True or false?*

*13. The word "satellite" comes from a Latin word for: a) attendant; b) star; c) spacecraft.*

*14. Which country was the first to launch a satellite?*

*15. Yuri Gagarin was the first man: a) on the Moon; b) to go into space; c) to drive his spaceship into a satellite.*

### Did you know?

When astronomers look at stars, they are seeing many of them as they were thousands or millions of years ago. Some of these stars may even no longer exist. Starlight takes this long to reach Earth because distances in space are so huge.

# What are things made of ?

**Everything in the world, from mountains and oceans, to air and animals, is made of chemicals.**

## What are chemicals?

All chemicals are made up of minute particles called atoms. The simplest chemicals are made of only one kind of atom and are called elements. Chemicals made up of two or more elements are called compounds. There are around one hundred elements, and over ten million compounds. New compounds are being discovered all the time.

**Glass is a compound made of the elements silicon, sodium and oxygen.**

**Water is a compound made of the elements hydrogen and oxygen.**

**Copper, which is used in electrical wiring, is an element.**

**The mercury in a thermometer is an element.**

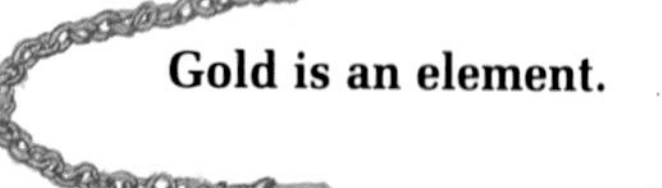

**Gold is an element.**

**Helium is an element. It makes balloons float up in the air.**

**Sand is a compound made of the elements silicon and oxygen.**

*1. Which one of the elements above used to be called quicksilver?*

Although food, wood and plastic are very different, most contain the same three elements: hydrogen, carbon and oxygen. What makes them different is the way their atoms have joined together to form larger particles, called molecules, and how these molecules have arranged themselves.

*2. Diamonds and coal are both made from the same element. True or false?*

*3. Which of these is sand not used for: a) making glass; b) putting out fires; c) seasoning food?*

## What makes something a solid, a liquid or a gas?

Atoms and the molecules they form are always moving, even in things that look still. Whether something is a solid, liquid or gas depends on how much these molecules are moving.

When water is solid ice, the water molecules are packed together evenly. These molecules are moving, but they are only vibrating.

When water is liquid, the molecules are close together, but are able to slip past each other. Liquids flow because the molecules can move around and change places with each other.

### How small is an atom?

Atoms are so small that if you magnified an atom to the size of a table tennis ball, the ball magnified by the same amount would be the size of the Earth.

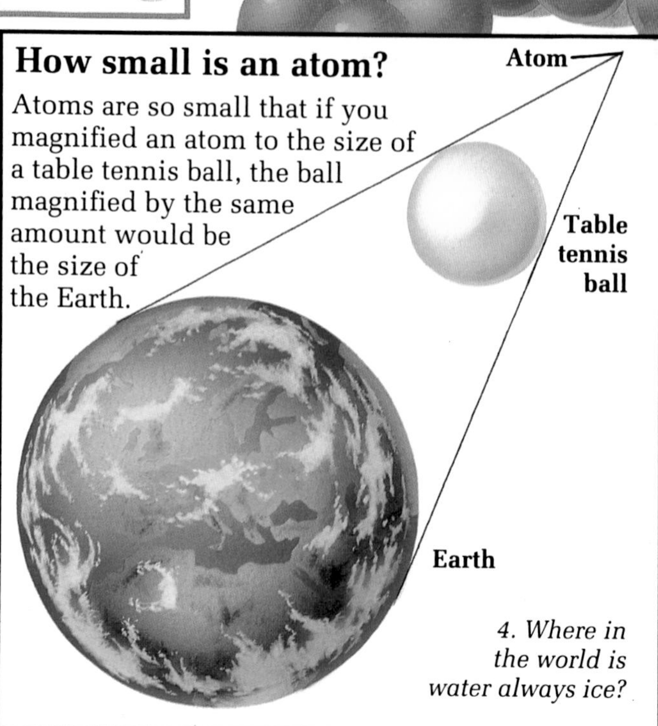


*4. Where in the world is water always ice?*

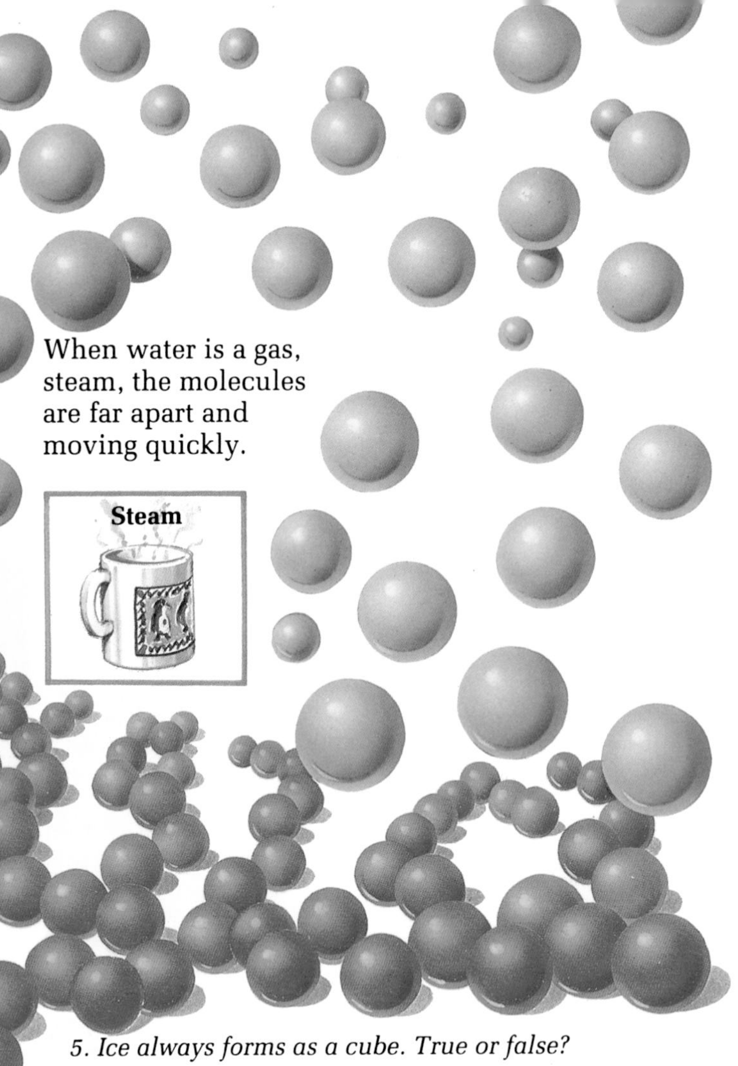


When water is a gas, steam, the molecules are far apart and moving quickly.

*5. Ice always forms as a cube. True or false?*

*6. Can iron be turned into a liquid?*

*7. Gas squashed into a smaller space is called: a) commendable; b) contaminated; c) compressed.*

## Did you know?

Ancient Greeks guessed that everything was made of atoms two and a half thousand years ago. The word "atom" comes from the Greek word *atomos* which means "uncuttable".

## Is anything smaller than an atom?

Atoms are made of even smaller particles called protons, neutrons and electrons.

**Protons and neutrons are found in the middle, or nucleus, of an atom.**

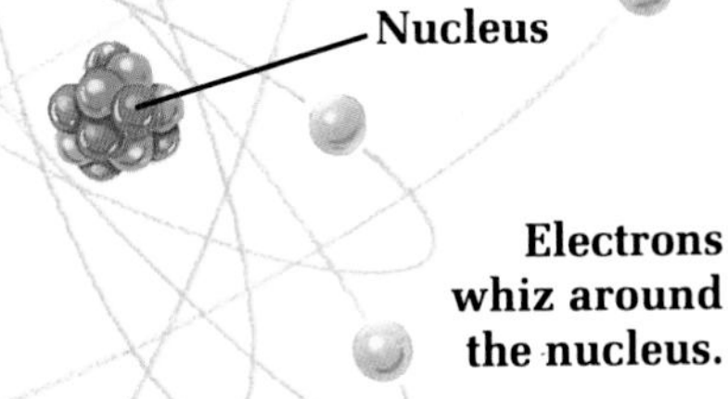


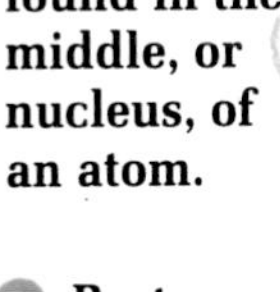


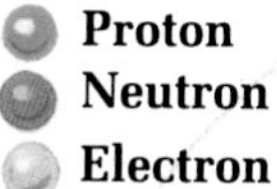


**Electrons whiz around the nucleus.**

Elements such as gold and mercury are different from one another because their atoms have a different number of electrons and protons.

*8. Electrons carry: a) specks of dust; b) an electrical charge; c) water molecules.*

## What is nuclear energy?

Nuclear energy (also called atomic energy) is stored in the nucleus in the middle of an atom. This energy can be released in the form of heat, in two ways. Large atoms can be split in two, or small atoms can be joined to other small atoms. Nuclear energy can be used to make electricity and very powerful weapons.

Nuclear power stations produce energy by heating steam which drives turbines to make electricity.

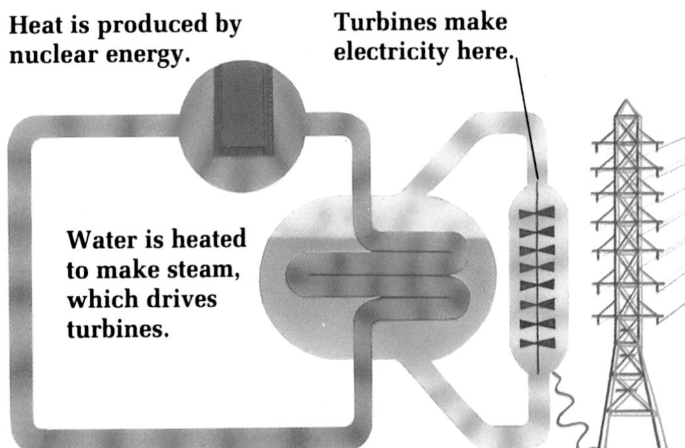


Nuclear bombs produce huge amounts of heat and are tremendously destructive. Some are so powerful that just one could destroy an entire city.

*9. Which of these metals is used to make nuclear energy: a) uranium; b) iron; c) copper?*

*10. Nuclear bombs have only been used against one country. Do you know which one?*

## Can you see atoms?

It is possible to see atoms with a scanning electron microscope. This can magnify up to around 50 million times by passing a stream of electrons through an object, which then strike a screen. A computer turns the pattern the electrons make into a picture, in which individual atoms are depicted.

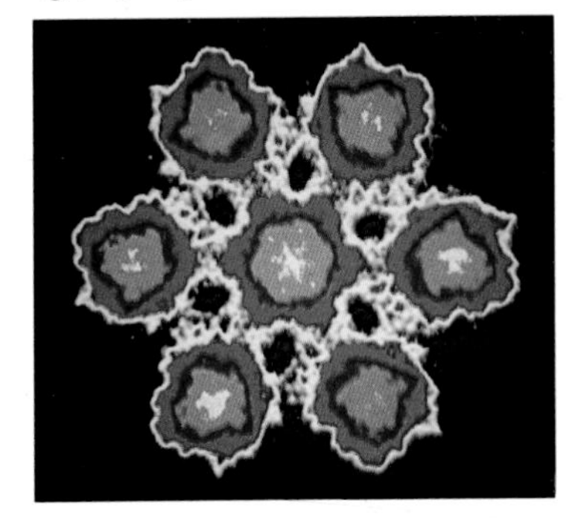

*11. A microscope which uses lenses to magnify is called an: a) oracle; b) electrical; c) optical microscope.*

*12. All nuclear energy is man-made. True or false?*

*13. Are smells solids, liquids or gases?*

*14. Which squashed gas do divers, astronauts and firemen carry in tanks, to enable them to breathe?*

*15. Unravel each of these words to make the names of three elements: dogl, propec, geynox.*

# Using materials

**The earth and sea are full of useful substances which are called raw materials. Raw materials are the basic ingredients for anything that people make.**

## What are raw materials?

Raw materials are natural materials. Most look different from the products they are used to make. Metals, for example, come from rocks called ores. This diagram shows some raw materials and their products.

*1. Can you match these raw materials with their products?*

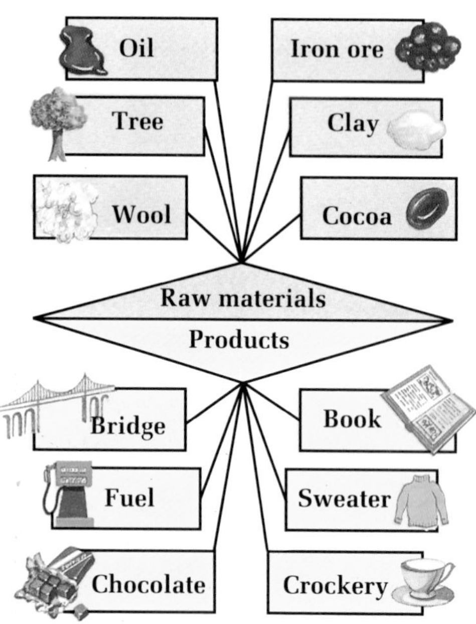


*2. Which one of these is a man-made material: a) wool; b) copper; c) nylon?*

## How are new materials made from raw materials?

Some raw materials, such as wood, can be used as they are. Others, such as metal ores, contain useful chemicals which have to be extracted before they can be used. This can be done with heat, or by combining the raw material with other chemicals.

Ores generally produce only one product: the metal inside them. Oil, called crude oil in its natural state, is more complex. It contains thousands of chemicals which can be turned into millions of products.

## How are new materials made from oil?

The thousands of chemicals in oil can be separated, or refined, by a process called fractional distillation. Many of the products of distillation, such as diesel oil, can be used as they are, but many others need further refining. This diagram shows how a distillation tower works.

*3. Which area is famous for producing crude oil: a) Texas, USA; b) the North Pole; c) Paris, France?*

*4. Does cooking oil come from crude oil?*

**1. Crude oil is heated to a very high temperature, and most of it enters the distillation tower as a gas.**

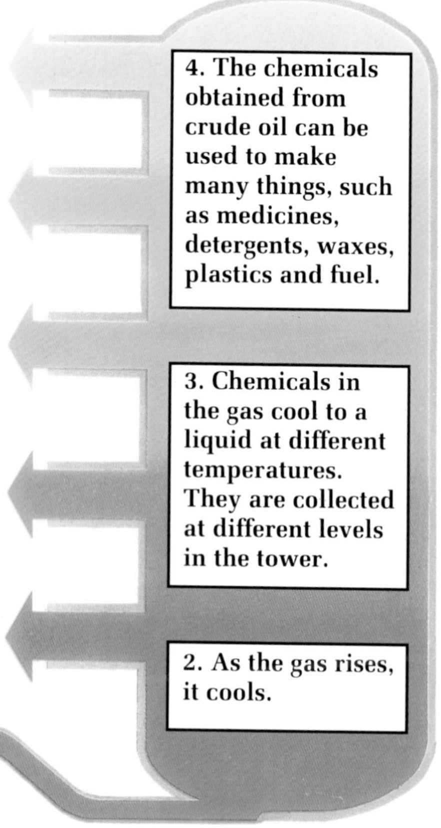

**2. As the gas rises, it cools.**

**3. Chemicals in the gas cool to a liquid at different temperatures. They are collected at different levels in the tower.**

**4. The chemicals obtained from crude oil can be used to make many things, such as medicines, detergents, waxes, plastics and fuel.**

## How are materials used?

When designers create a product, they specify the most suitable materials for the job. For example, in motor racing, materials are chosen to keep the driver safe and also to help the car perform well. This picture shows how some of these materials are used in the car and clothing of a top racing driver. Many of the materials come from metal ores and crude oil, but plant and animal materials are also used.

The car body is made of a mixture, or composite, of man-made materials known as plastics. One of these plastics is called Kevlar*, which comes from the chemicals in crude oil. Kevlar gives the car strength. It is a very useful material because not only is it strong and rigid, it is also very light. It has many other uses, such as in the manufacture of bulletproof vests and the bodies of boats and aircraft.

*5. Why is it important that the car is light in weight?*

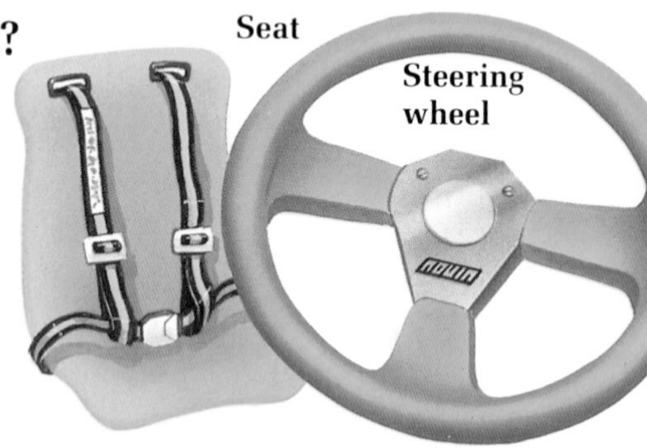


The seat and steering wheel are covered in suede, a velvety kind of leather. Suede helps the driver grip.

The tyres are mainly made of rubber, which grips the track well. Layers of steel and fabric give strength and flexibility.

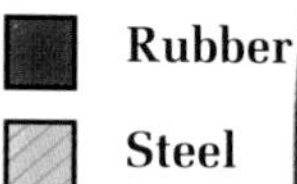
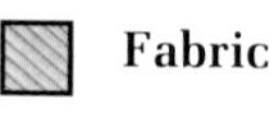


*6. What kind of raw material is rubber made from?*

*Du Pont's registered trademark

## How is metal taken from ores?

There are about 80 known metals. A few, such as gold, exist on their own, but most are found within ores, which are mined.

Metals are extracted from their ore by heating them with other materials. The atoms in these substances are rearranged to make new substances. This process is called a chemical reaction.

The diagram shows how iron is extracted from iron ore by a process called smelting.

*10. More than three-quarters of elements are metals. True or false?*

*11. This type of furnace is called an: a) open; b) closed; c) blast furnace.*

*12. Some metals explode if they are dropped in water. True or false?*

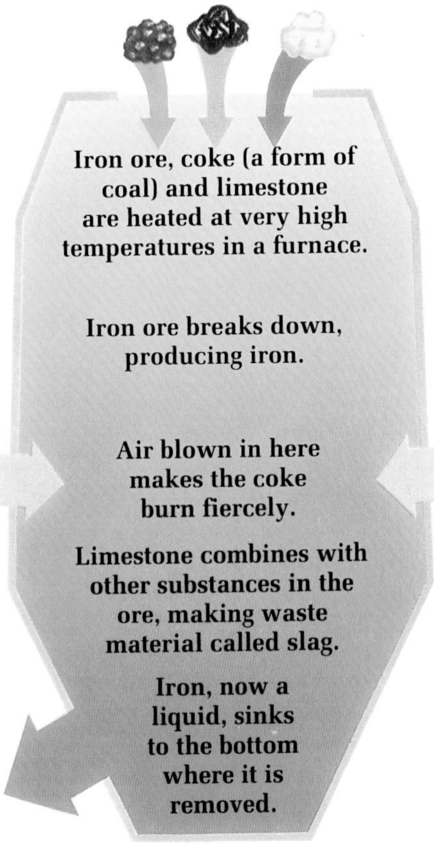

**Iron ore, coke (a form of coal) and limestone are heated at very high temperatures in a furnace.**

**Iron ore breaks down, producing iron.**

**Air blown in here makes the coke burn fiercely.**

**Limestone combines with other substances in the ore, making waste material called slag.**

**Iron, now a liquid, sinks to the bottom where it is removed.**

### Did you know?

Gold is such a precious metal that scientists, known as alchemists, spent centuries trying to turn cheap metals, such as lead, into gold. They failed, but their work became the basis of our knowledge of metals and alloys today.

*13. The purity of gold is measured in: a) lead; b) pearls; c) carats.*

*14. Alchemists are named after Al the Chemist – the first man to try to turn lead into gold. True or false?*

*15. A thin sheet of gold is called gold: a) leaf; b) sheaf; c) reef.*

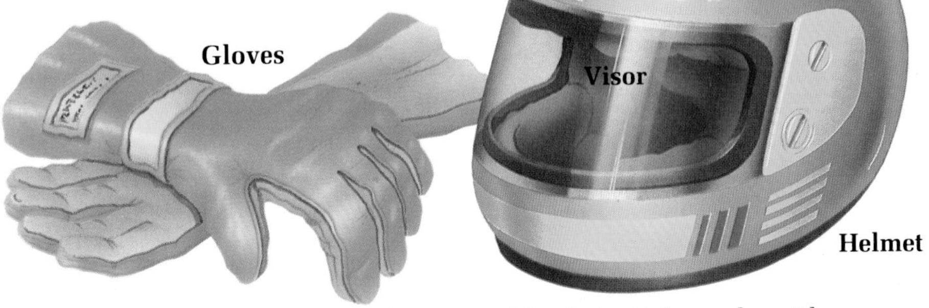

**Gloves**

**Visor**

**Helmet**

The driver's suit and gloves are made from another oil product: a light, fire-resistant material called Nomex*. Fire-fighters and astronauts also wear Nomex suits.

*7. Why is the driver's suit fire-resistant?*

*8. Can crude oil be used directly in cars as fuel?*

Parts of the car, including the engine and spring suspension, are made from alloys: combinations of metals and other materials. Alloys are stronger than pure metals. The suspension springs are made of the alloy steel, a combination of iron and carbon.

The helmet is made with Kevlar, and the visor is made of Lexan**, a light, tough plastic produced from chemicals in crude oil. Thin, plastic covers, which the driver tears off as each one gets dirty, are fixed to the visor.

*9. People first made alloys in the: a) Ice; b) Bronze; c) Space Age.*

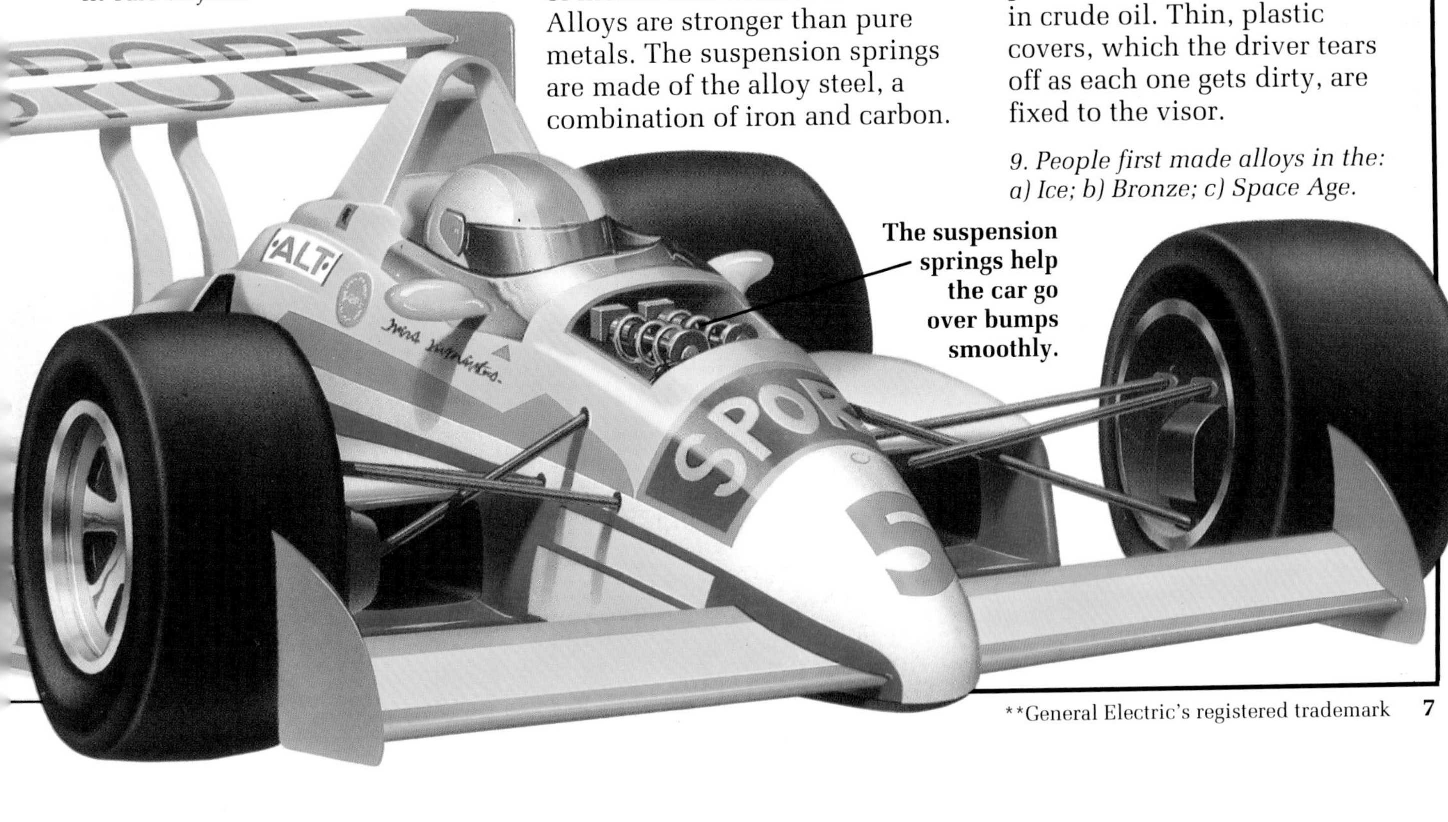

**General Electric's registered trademark

# Moving, flying and floating

**Deep in space, a moving object will carry on at the same speed, in the same direction endlessly. This does not happen on Earth. Forces act on everything, making them speed up, slow down, change direction and even change shape.**

## What is a force?

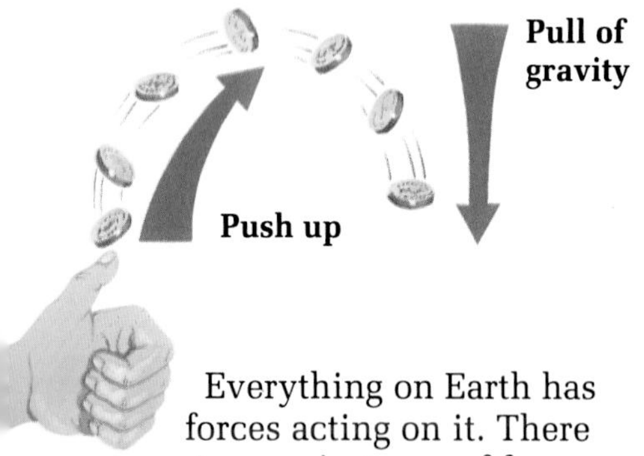

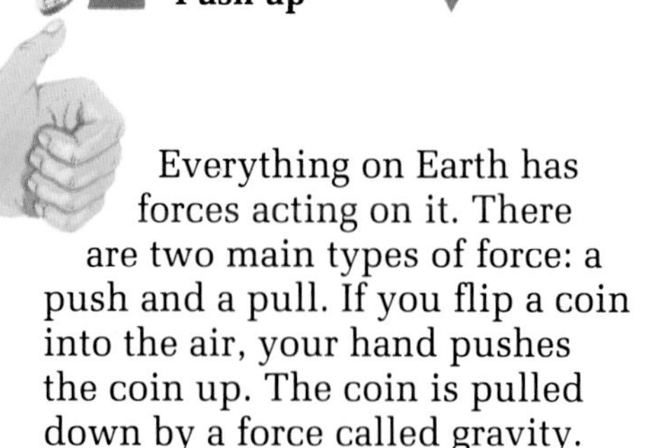


Everything on Earth has forces acting on it. There are two main types of force: a push and a pull. If you flip a coin into the air, your hand pushes the coin up. The coin is pulled down by a force called gravity.

## What is gravity?

Gravity pulls all objects towards one another. However, it is a weak force. Only huge objects, such as planets, have a strong enough gravity to pull things to them.

Gravity pulls everything towards the middle of the Earth. Things are not sucked in because the ground pushes up against them. Gravity, like all forces, has an opposite force working against it.

*1. Astronauts on the way to the Moon go most of the way with their rocket engines switched off. True or false?*

## What makes things heavy or light?

How heavy something is depends on how big it is, how heavy its atoms are, and how closely these atoms are packed together. A steel ball weighs more than an apple of the same size because its atoms are heavier: it is said to have a greater density. It feels heavier because gravity pulls harder on denser materials.

*2. Is stone more dense than chocolate?*

*3. Steel is made from copper and lead. True or false?*

## How do forces work?

This picture shows how forces act on a bike when you are riding along. The different forces affect how the bike moves and how fast it is able to go.

1. The force of the Earth's gravity pulls the bike down against the road.

2. The ground pushes in the opposite direction against the wheels of the bike.

3. As you turn the pedals, the wheels are pushed around. The wheels push the bike forwards.

4. Air pushes in the opposite direction to your body and the bike, as you ride along.

*4. In a race, why do cyclists crouch down low over the handlebars?*

*5. Which type of bike is made for two riders: a) a tandem; b) a unicycle; c) a tricycle?*

## What makes things slow down?

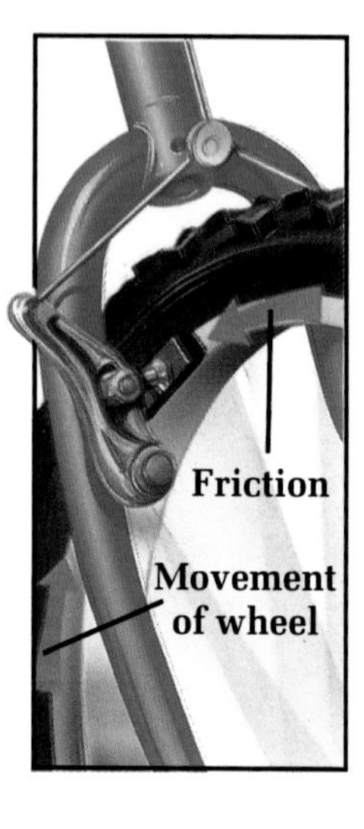


Objects pushing against each other, such as a wheel pushing against the ground, create a force called friction. Friction slows moving objects down. It also produces heat. This is why bike wheels feel hot when you have been riding. Some of the bike's energy is turned into heat instead of moving the wheels, which slows the bike down.

Brakes work using friction. When you work the brakes on a bike, the brake blocks are pulled against the wheel rims. Friction acts between them, bringing the bike to a halt.

*6. Would you feel more friction on ice or on gravel?*

*7. You can get a friction burn from: a) a candle flame; b) boiling water; c) sliding down a rope.*

## Where does energy go?

When energy is used, it changes into another form of energy. Energy never goes away and new energy is never made. Even energy that seems to fade to nothing, such as the sound of your voice, is not lost: it just spreads out further and further as tiny vibrations.

Fireworks are stores of chemical energy. When they explode, the chemical energy is suddenly turned into sound, light, heat and kinetic energy.

When a cat pounces, the chemical energy stored within its body is turned into kinetic energy. When animals move, their muscles also produce heat energy.

Light energy
Heat energy
Sound energy
Kinetic energy
Chemical energy

A cat stores chemical energy from its food.

Chemical energy is turned into kinetic energy and heat.

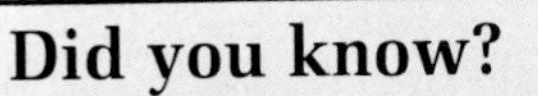

## Did you know?

Around 70% of the energy in fuels is lost when they are used to produce electricity. This is because some energy escapes as heat each time energy changes form. At a power station, energy has to change three times, from fuel to heat, to movement and then to electricity. Heat escapes at each stage.

*10. What sorts of energy does a burning candle produce?*

*11. Which form of energy cannot travel through space: a) heat; b) light; c) sound?*

*12. Most light bulbs lose 95% of their energy as heat. True or false?*

## How is food turned into energy?

When you eat, food is broken down, or digested, in your stomach and intestines. It is then absorbed into your blood, which is pumped around your body to your muscles.

In your muscles, energy is released from food by a process like very slow burning, called respiration. Respiration, like burning, needs oxygen. This is why you breathe.

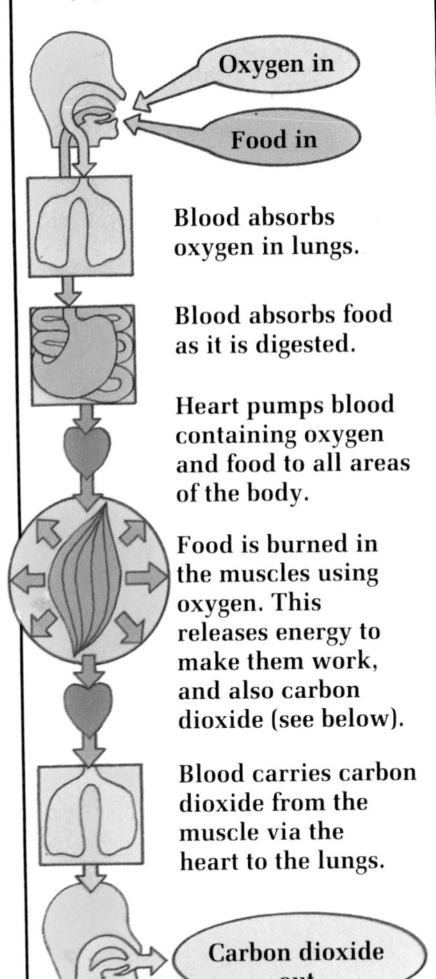


When fuel burns, it produces a gas called carbon dioxide. Your blood carries the carbon dioxide produced in your muscles back to your heart, which pumps it to your lungs so you can breathe it out.

*13. Energy in food is measured in: a) calories; b) watts; c) grams.*

*14. Who has more stored energy, a fat person or a thin person?*

*15. Do you use energy when you are asleep?*

# Electricity and magnetism

**Electricity and magnetism are forms of energy, like sound and light. They have an effect on each other that can be put to many uses, from driving an electric motor to powering a computer.**

## What is electricity?

Electricity is made from electrons: the particles that make up the outside of an atom (see page 5).

In some materials, the electrons can move easily from atom to atom. This flow of electrons is called electricity. It occurs naturally, and it can also be man-made.

Materials that electrons can pass through easily, such as metals, are called conductors. Copper is used in electrical wiring because it is a good conductor. Materials which electrons cannot pass through, such as plastic, are called insulators.

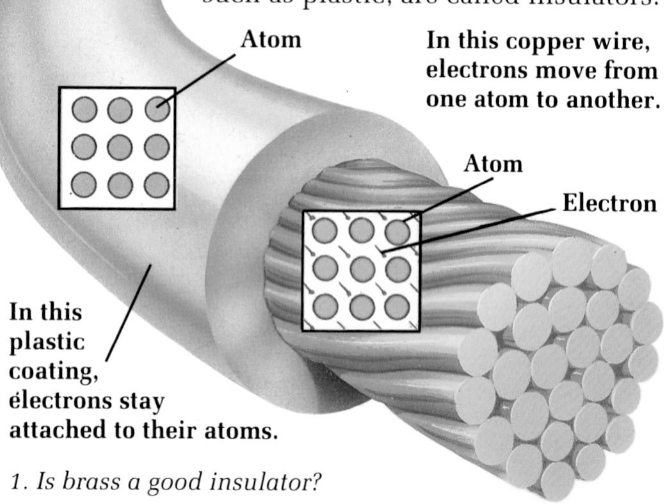


*1. Is brass a good insulator?*

### Did you know?

Electricity produces heat and fires can start if electrical wiring overheats. Fire-fighters use foam instead of water to put out electrical fires. This is because water conducts electricity and could give the fire-fighters electric shocks.

## What causes lightning?

Lightning is caused by static electricity. This is the same kind of electricity as man-made electricity but it is made in a different way. It happens naturally when two materials rub against each other.

*3. Thunder is the noise made when lightning hits the ground. True or false?*

*4. Does lightning hit the highest or lowest point on the ground beneath it?*

Lightning occurs when water and air particles in a cloud rub against each other. An electrical force, or charge, builds up and jumps to the Earth, or another cloud, in a huge flash.

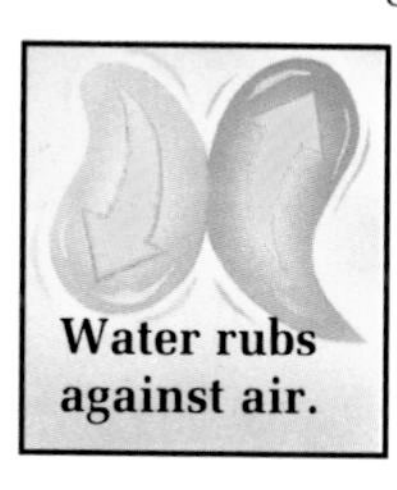

*5. Which one of the following can be caused by static electricity: a) hair standing up on end; b) fireworks; c) torrential rain?*

If you walk on a nylon carpet and drag your feet, electrons jump from the carpet to your feet. This causes an electrical charge to build up on your body. When you touch a metal object, the static electricity jumps over to it, giving you a tiny electric shock.

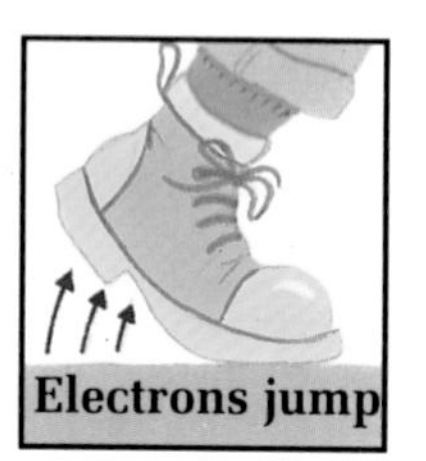

*6. Lightning never strikes in the same place twice. True or false?*

*7. Tiny electric shocks keep you alive. True or false?*

*8. Which of these would help prevent electric shocks: a) rubber boots; b) steel helmet; c) cotton socks?*

*9. Why is it unsafe to use an electrical appliance when your hands are wet?*

## How does electricity get to your home?

Electrons do not move along a wire by themselves, they are pushed along by a force. Power stations create this force, which is measured in volts.

Power station

Heat from a nuclear reaction, for example, turns water to steam. The steam drives a turbine which spins a magnet in a coil of wire.

*2. Are all turbines powered by steam?*

This causes an electric current to flow in the coil. This device, called a generator, sends electricity from the power station along a wire cable.

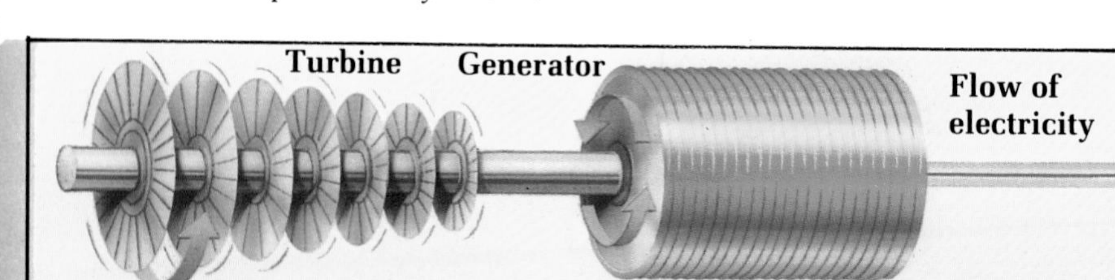

## How do magnets work?

In a magnet, there are millions of particles which all have a tiny magnetic force. These particles line up to point the same way, making a force strong enough to pull or push certain metals within the magnet's range, or field.

Only a few metals, such as iron, have magnetic particles. In iron, these particles can be lined up easily to make a magnet. If you hit it with a hammer, the particles no longer line up and the iron loses its magnetic force: it becomes demagnetized.

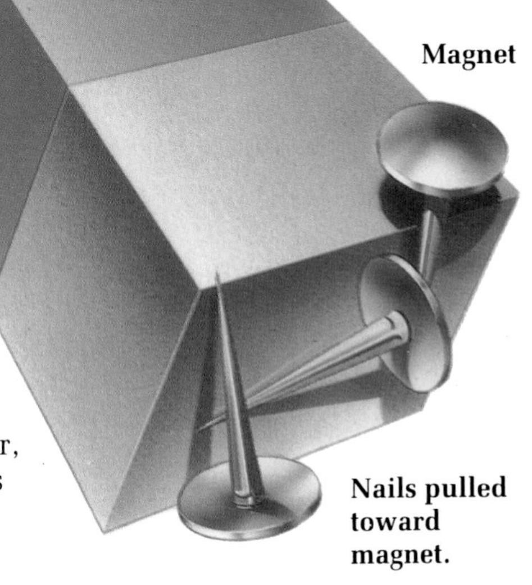


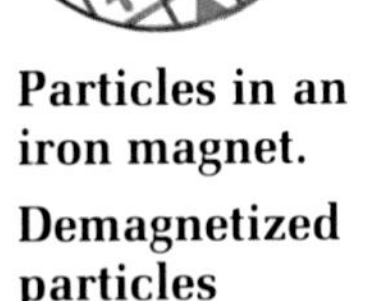
Particles in an iron magnet.

Demagnetized particles

*10. Can magnets pick up wood?*

*11. Is the Earth magnetic?*

*12. Does glue work by magnetism?*

## How does a junk-yard magnet work?

Powerful magnets, which can be switched on and off, are used to move heavy pieces of metal around junk yards. These magnets, called electromagnets, work because an electric current flowing along a wire creates a magnetic field. This effect is called electromagnetism. It is used to work many machines in factories and homes.

An electromagnet is made by coiling electrical wire around a bar of easily magnetized metal, such as iron. When the current is switched on, the magnetism of the metal bar and the wire coil combine.

So, when the operator of a junk-yard magnet wants to pick up metal, the magnet is switched on. The operator can then move the metal by swinging the giant magnet. When the operator wants to drop the metal, the current is switched off.

**Electrical wire coiled around magnet.**

*13. Electrical power is measured in: a) Whys; b) Sparks; c) Watts.*

## How does an electric motor work?

If a coil of wire is put inside a magnetic field and the current switched on, the coil is attracted by the magnetic field around it, which makes it spin. The spin of the wire coil can drive a machine. This device is called an electric motor. Electric motors are used in many machines such as an electric fan, or a food blender.

**Magnet**

**Spindle turns blades.**

**Wire coil**

**Blades turn, circulating air in the room.**

*14. Which one of these electric devices uses an electric motor: a) kettle; b) light bulb; c) doorbell; d) washing machine?*

*15. Electric motors were invented in: a) 1421; b) 1621; c) 1821.*

At home, electricity is fed into a meter which records how much is used. It also flows through a fuse, a narrow wire which melts if the current is too strong.

The wires and machines that electricity flows through are called a circuit. All parts of a circuit must connect for electricity to flow.

Switches control electricity in the circuit. Switching on or off completes or breaks the circuit, working a radio, for example.

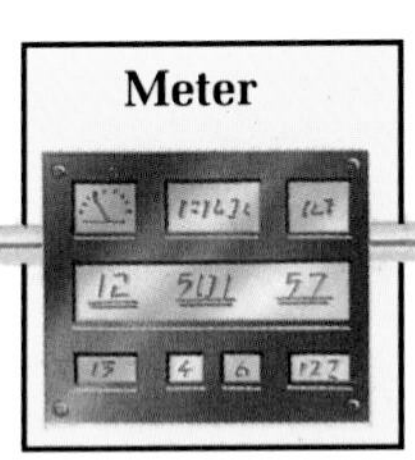


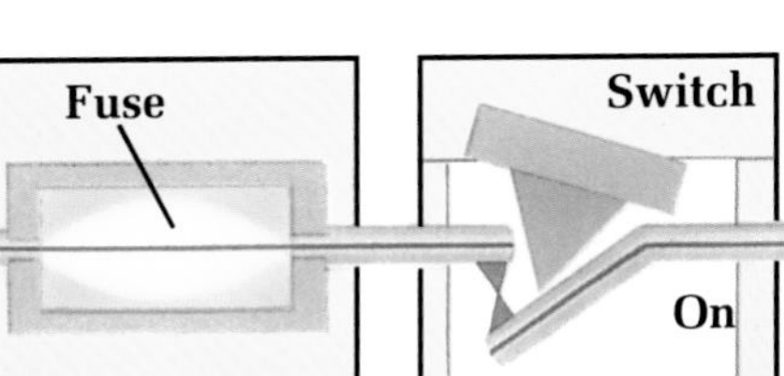

# Sound and music

**Sound is a kind of energy which travels through air, water and solid objects such as walls and the ground. Most types of sound contain only a small amount of energy.**

## How are sounds made?

Sounds happen when the tiny particles that make up the air are made to move back and forth very quickly. This movement is called vibration.

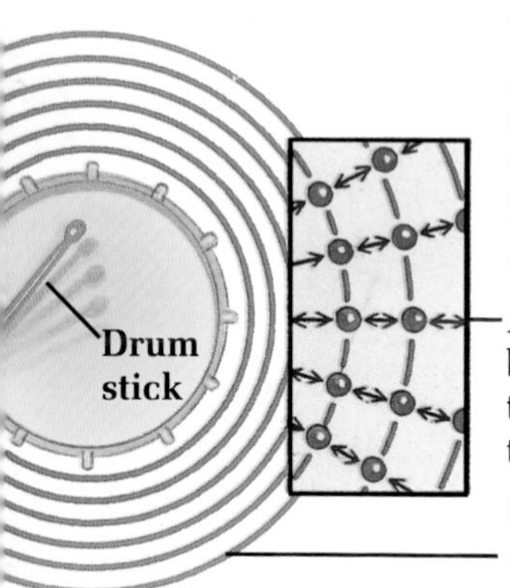


**When a drum is hit, the skin vibrates and bumps into air particles.**

**Air particles bump into the ones next to them.**

**Sound travels as waves of vibrating air.**

The waves travel in an expanding circle. Strong vibrations make loud noises and gentle ones make quiet noises.

*1. Which has more energy, the sound of a handclap or a clap of thunder?*

*2. The loudness of a sound is measured in: a) handbels; b) loudbels; c) decibels.*

*3. Can sound travel around corners?*

## What makes sounds different?

When air particles vibrate quickly, the sound waves travel close together. You hear them as a high-pitched sound, such as a bird's chirrup.

If air particles vibrate slowly, the sound waves are further apart. You hear them as a low-pitched sound, such as the chugging of a truck. The speed of vibration is called frequency.

## What is an echo?

When sound waves hit a solid surface, such as a cliff, some travel through it. Others bounce back, like waves in the sea bouncing back off the cliff.

Sound waves travel back through the air towards the source of the original sound. You then hear the sound again, as an echo. Short, loud noises make the best echoes.

Fishing boats find shoals of fish by sending high-pitched sounds down into the sea. The sounds echo back off the fish, and a computer on board interprets the echoes, locating the fish.

*7. Can children hear higher frequencies than adults?*

*8. Would you hear an echo better on a windy day or a calm day?*

**High-frequency sound**

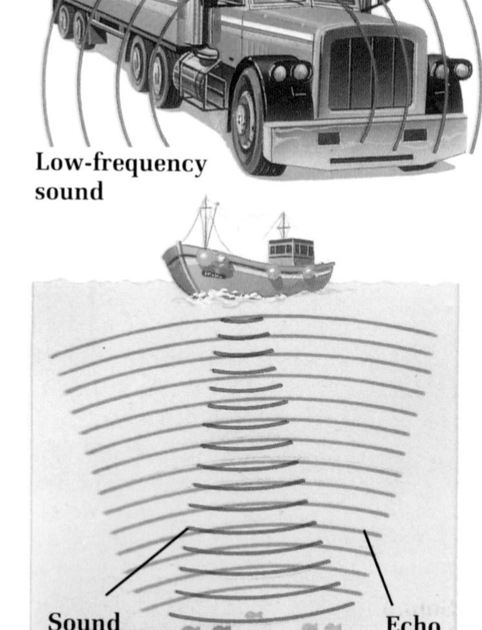


*9. Some sounds are so loud they are able to travel around the world. True or false?*

*10. Locating objects by listening to echoes of high-frequency sound is called: a) radar; b) sonar; c) laser.*

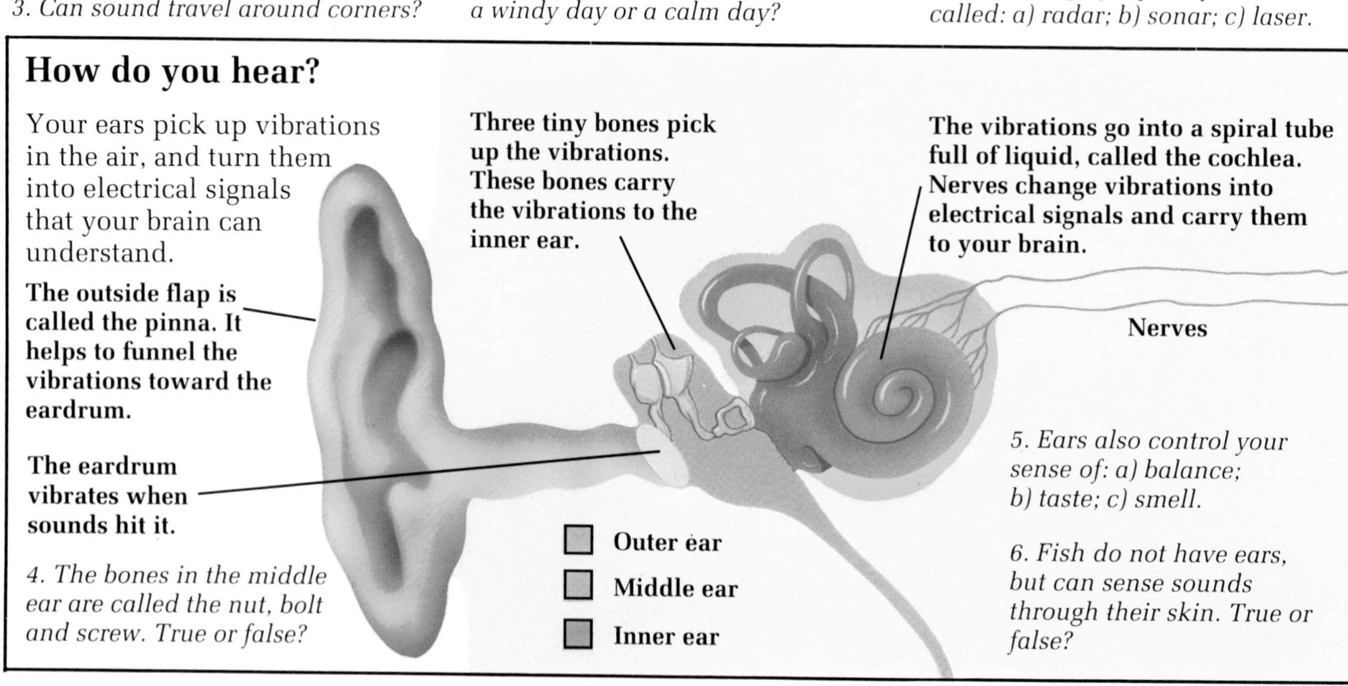

## How do you hear?

Your ears pick up vibrations in the air, and turn them into electrical signals that your brain can understand.

**The outside flap is called the pinna. It helps to funnel the vibrations toward the eardrum.**

**The eardrum vibrates when sounds hit it.**

*4. The bones in the middle ear are called the nut, bolt and screw. True or false?*

**Three tiny bones pick up the vibrations. These bones carry the vibrations to the inner ear.**

**The vibrations go into a spiral tube full of liquid, called the cochlea. Nerves change vibrations into electrical signals and carry them to your brain.**



*5. Ears also control your sense of: a) balance; b) taste; c) smell.*

*6. Fish do not have ears, but can sense sounds through their skin. True or false?*

## What sounds do animals hear?

Many large animals, such as elephants, can hear lower sounds than people, but not the high sounds that we do. Many small animals, such as shrews and bats, can hear and make higher sounds than people. Bats listen to the echoes of the sounds they make, to find insects to eat.

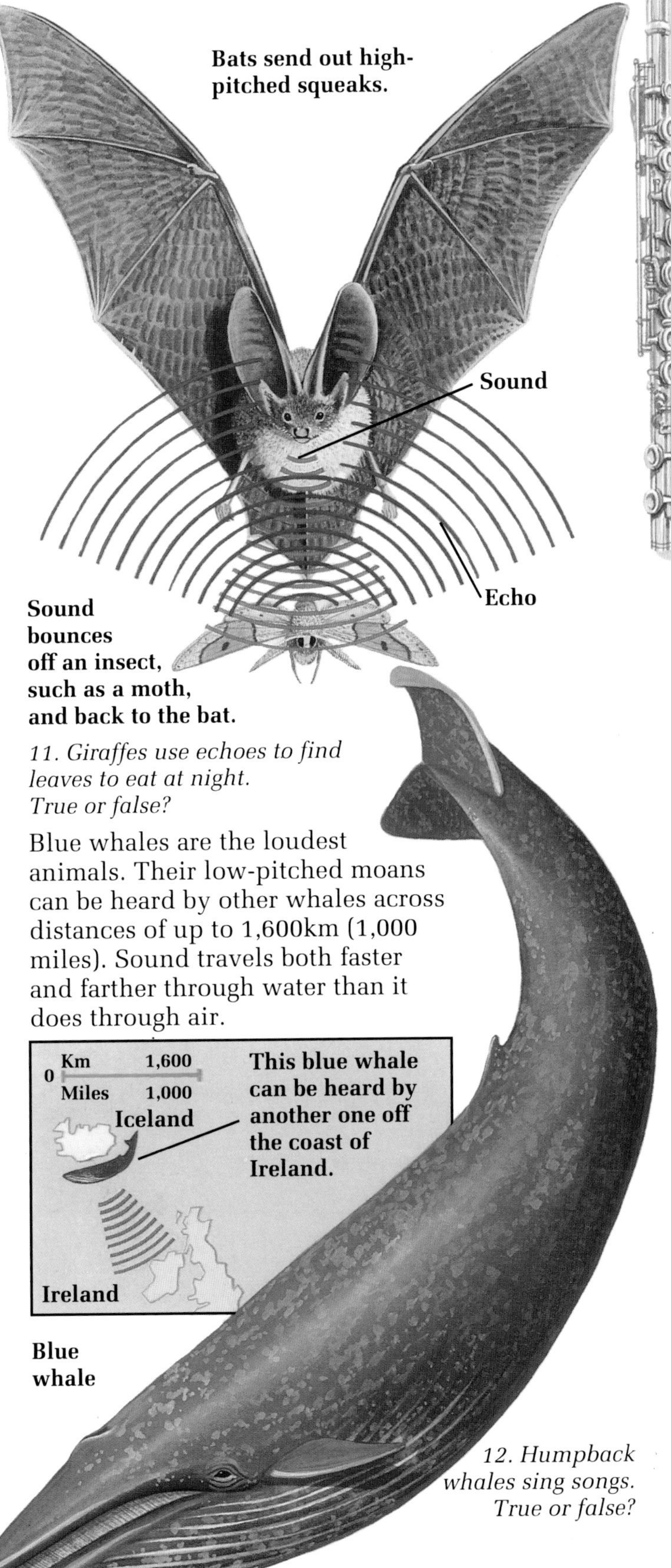


*11. Giraffes use echoes to find leaves to eat at night. True or false?*

Blue whales are the loudest animals. Their low-pitched moans can be heard by other whales across distances of up to 1,600km (1,000 miles). Sound travels both faster and farther through water than it does through air.



**This blue whale can be heard by another one off the coast of Ireland.**

**Blue whale**

*12. Humpback whales sing songs. True or false?*

## What makes instruments sound different?

Musical instruments sound different because they make vibrations in different ways. Their shape, the materials they are made of, and how they are played, affect the way that they vibrate. This gives each instrument its own range of notes and its own distinctive tone.

Musical notes all have a similar pattern. They begin, build up to full volume and then fade away. The time that each stage takes depends on the instrument and the way the player controls the note. The graph below shows an example of the shape of a flute note.

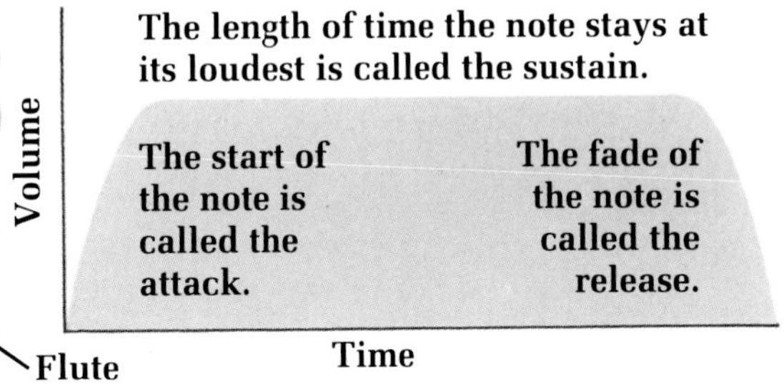

**The length of time the note stays at its loudest is called the sustain.**

**Volume**

**The start of the note is called the attack.**

**The fade of the note is called the release.**

**Time**

**Flute**

Wind instruments, such as the flute, have a fairly quick attack and release. The note sustains for as long as the player blows. The graph below shows the shape of another note, played on a guitar.

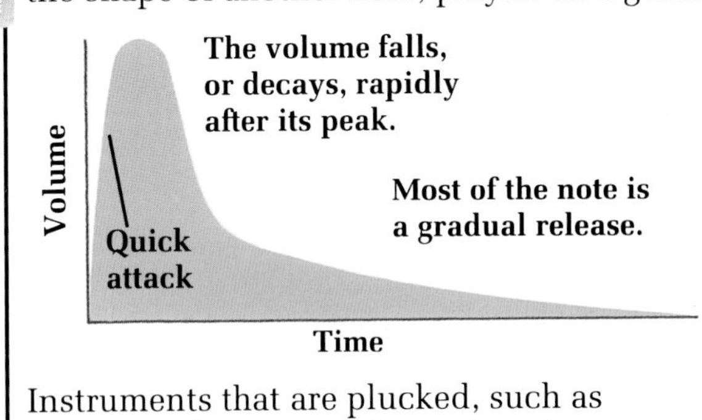


Instruments that are plucked, such as the guitar, have a quick attack and no sustain. There is a long release as the string gradually stops vibrating.

**Guitar**

*13. Drums, cymbals and xylophones are all: a) percussion instruments; b) percolated instruments; c) polystyrene instruments.*

*14. Unravel each of these words to make the names of four instruments: angor, batu, napio, tirgua.*

## Did you know?

There are no sounds in space. This is because there is no air for sound waves to travel through. Without air, water or solid particles to vibrate, there is no noise. In space, astronauts talk to each other by radio.

*15. Any place, such as outer space, where there is no air is called: a) air-tight; b) arid; c) a vacuum.*

# Light and colour

**Light is a form of energy, which enables us to see the things around us. It is released by sources of heat, such as the Sun, a light bulb or a candle.**

**Light is made up of seven different colours – red, orange, yellow, green, blue, indigo and violet. These colours normally merge together, so that you cannot see them separately.**

## What is a rainbow?

Light travels in waves and the wavelengths of the seven colours are all slightly different. A rainbow appears when the colours are split apart.

**Light waves are so small that around 40 thousand of them would fit in this wavelength here.**

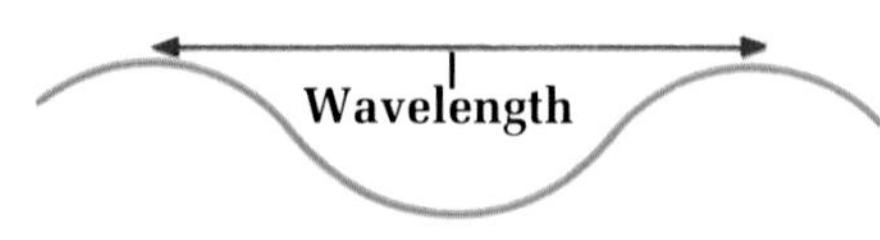


If light enters a transparent substance (such as glass or water) directly, it travels straight through. However, if it enters at an angle, it bends. This is called refraction. At some angles, the seven colours all bend in a slightly different direction, so you can see them all. This is called dispersion.

You can see this effect if you shine light through a triangular glass block, called a prism. The prism is shaped to refract and disperse light.

Rainbows happen when the Sun shines when it is raining, or just after a shower. Sunlight travels through the raindrops and is refracted and dispersed.

**Each colour travels in a slightly different direction.**

Prism

Light

Red

Orange

Yellow

Green

Blue

Indigo

Violet

## How do you see colour?

When light waves hit objects, they bounce back. This is called reflection. Objects appear to be different colours because they reflect some of the colours in light and absorb others. When light shines on an object, the reflected colours bounce back into your eyes.

This T-shirt is black because it absorbs all the colours in light. It reflects hardly any light.

This plant appears green because it only reflects green light and no other colours.

This rabbit appears white because it reflects all the colours in white light equally well.

*4. All animals see in black and white. True or false?*
*5. Some animals make light. True or false?*
*6. What colours does snow reflect?*

## What makes the sky blue?

When sunlight hits the Earth's atmosphere, it begins to break up and blue light is scattered all over the sky. This happens because the upper atmosphere contains gas and dust particles which are about the same size as the wavelength of blue light. This causes blue light to bounce off them.

**At midday, blue light is scattered over the sky.**

The atmosphere gets thicker the nearer it is to the Earth's surface, and as light travels through it, more light is scattered. Light with shorter wavelengths, like blue and violet are scattered most.

At sunset or sunrise, sunlight travels through much more of the atmosphere before it reaches you. Most of its colours are scattered by the time it reaches the lower atmosphere. Only reds and oranges are left.

*7. The sea is blue because: a) it contains blue seaweed; b) squid squirt blue dye; c) it reflects the sky.*

*8. Can light travel through space?*

**At sunset, only red and orange light can be seen.**

*1. If red and yellow are mixed together, do they make: a) blue; b) green; c) orange?*

*2. Another name for the colours of the rainbow is: a) a spatula; b) a spectrum; c) a sporran.*

*3. Can light travel around corners?*

## How does a mirror work?

Light waves reflect in a similar way to a ball bouncing. For example, when a tennis ball hits a smooth clay court, it bounces evenly, leaving the surface of the court at the same angle at which it arrived. Light behaves like this when it hits a mirror. It travels through a smooth, glass layer and then bounces off a shiny, metal coating. Light waves all bounce back evenly, staying in the same order, which enables you to see a reflection.

If you play tennis on an uneven surface such as grass, balls hitting different bumps will bounce at different angles. Light behaves like this when it hits a dull, rough surface, such as wood. Light rays scatter in all directions.

*9. Ancient Egyptians used mirrors. True or false?*

*10. Can you see a reflection in polished wood?*

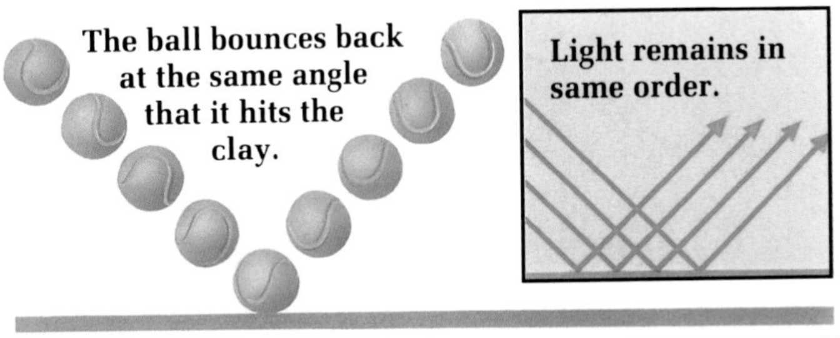

**The ball bounces back at the same angle that it hits the clay.**

**Light remains in same order.**

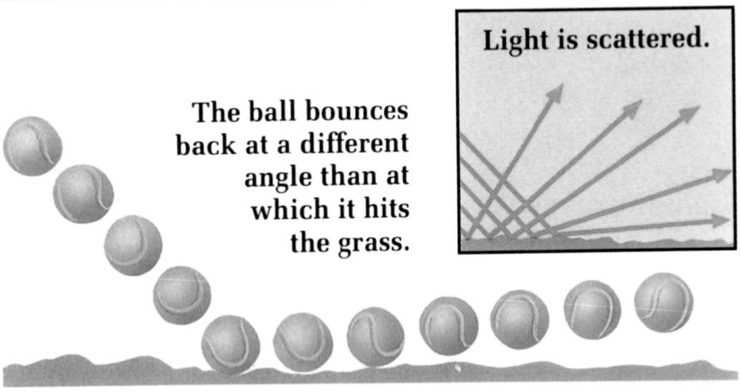

**Light is scattered.**

**The ball bounces back at a different angle than at which it hits the grass.**

## How do you see?

You see objects because light bounces off them and reflects into your eyes. This picture shows how what you see is turned into an image that your brain can recognize. Light enters through the pupil, a black hole at the front of the eye. The coloured area around the pupil, the iris, prevents harmful light rays from entering the eye. Light then passes through a transparent, rubbery disc, called a lens.

The lens helps you see more clearly, or focus, by bending light, so that it hits the back of the eye, which is called the retina. The lens turns what you see upside down. The retina is made up of millions of tiny cells which are called rods and cones. Rods are sensitive to dim light. Cones are sensitive to bright light and colour. There are over 130 million rods and cones in an eye. When light falls on them electrical messages are passed to the optic nerve.

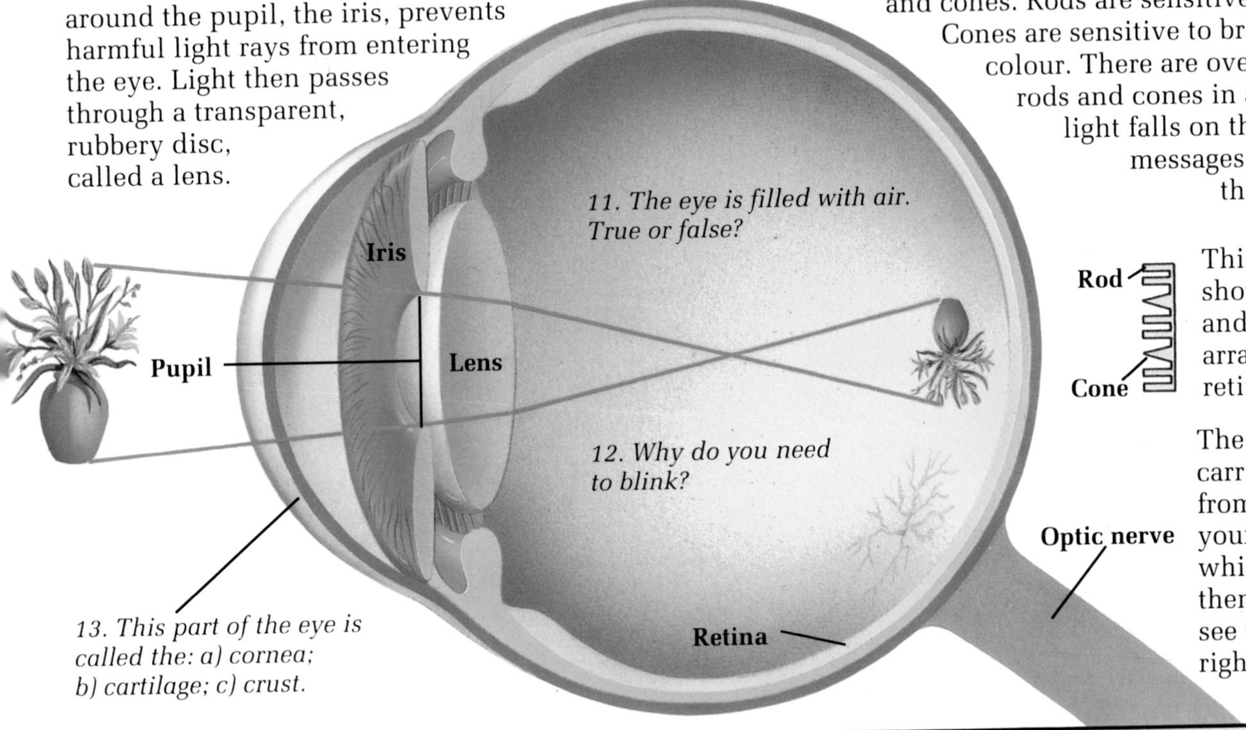

*11. The eye is filled with air. True or false?*

*12. Why do you need to blink?*

**Iris**

**Pupil**

**Lens**

**Retina**

**Optic nerve**

*13. This part of the eye is called the: a) cornea; b) cartilage; c) crust.*

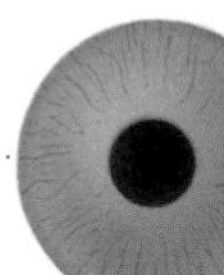

**Rod**

**Cone**

This diagram shows how rods and cones are arranged in the retina.

The optic nerve carries messages from the retina to your brain, which interprets them, so that you see things the right way up.

**In bright light, the iris closes up to protect your eyes.**

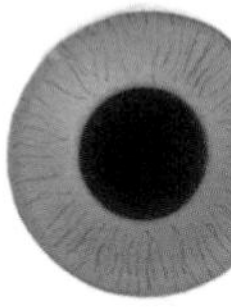

**In dim light, the iris opens up to let more light in, so you can see better.**

*14. Which two of these animals can see well in the dark: a) dogs; b) cats; c) owls; d) sheep; e) ducks?*

### Did you know?

Light travels quicker than anything in the Universe. Its speed is around 300,000km (186,000 miles) per second. This means that it takes eight minutes to travel the 150 million km (93 million miles) from the Sun to Earth.

*15. Which travels faster, thunder or lightning?*

# Living things

**There is life in almost every part of the world. The sky, sea, soil and surface of the Earth are full of plants and animals.**

## What makes something a living thing?

Living things have particular features which non-living things lack. For instance, they can react to their surroundings, they need energy to live and can reproduce. Below you can see the qualities which separate living things from non-living things.

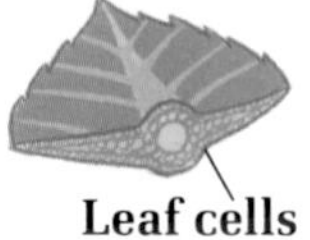


All living things are made up of tiny units, called cells.

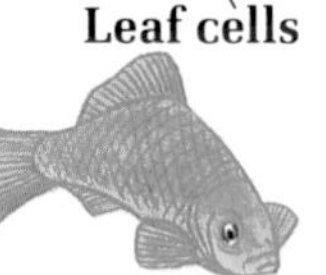

All living things need oxygen, which they get from air or water.

The bodies of living things produce waste, which they need to get rid of.

All animals can move part of their bodies. Flowers can open and close petals.

Almost all living things grow. Growth occurs when cells divide.

All living things reproduce so that new ones live on when they die.

All living things need food to give them energy to breed, move or grow.

All living things are aware of their surroundings and react to them.

*1. Which one of the following do plants not do: a) reproduce; b) make food; c) think; d) move?*

*2. An erupting volcano is a living thing. True or false?*

## What is the difference between an animal and a plant?

Here is how plants and animals differ.

### Food

The main difference between plants and animals is the way in which they get their food.

Animals eat plants or other animals, or both. The food is broken down in their bodies and gives them energy. This breakdown of food is called digestion.

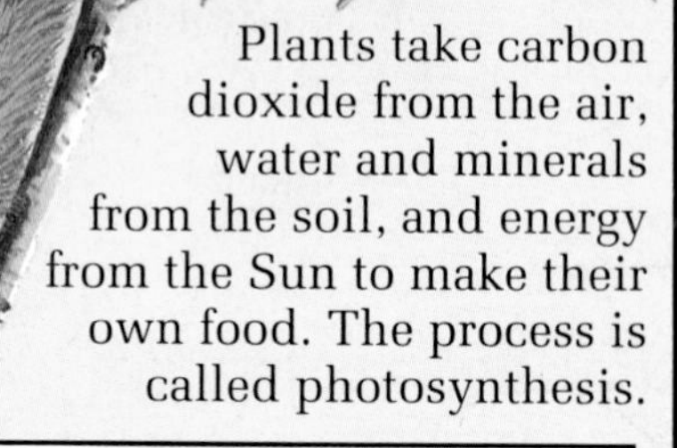

Plants take carbon dioxide from the air, water and minerals from the soil, and energy from the Sun to make their own food. The process is called photosynthesis.

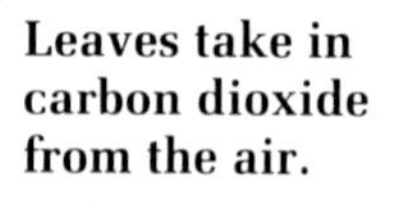


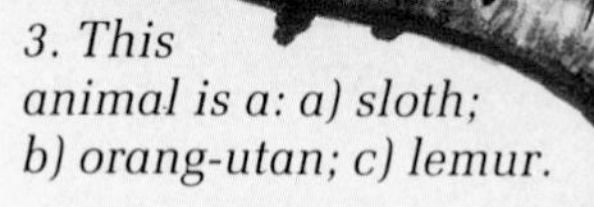

*3. This animal is a: a) sloth; b) orang-utan; c) lemur.*

### Cells

The cells in animals' bodies have soft walls.

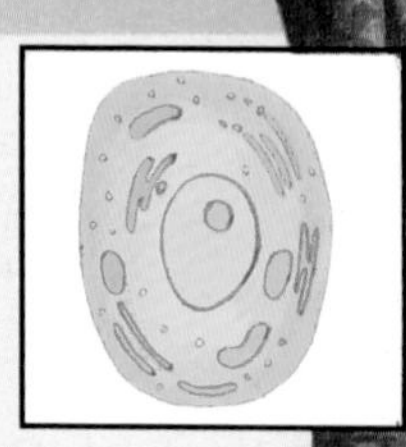

**Animal cell**

Plant cells have thick, tough walls.

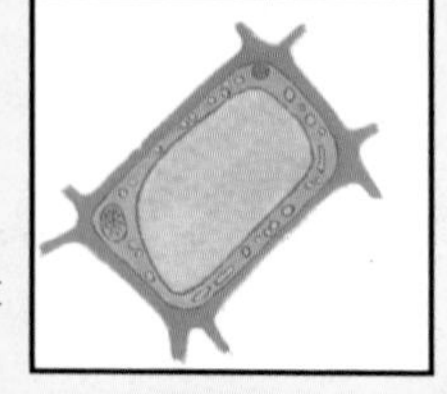

**Plant cell**

### Movement

Most animals can move their bodies around. They are more sensitive than plants and can react quickly to change.

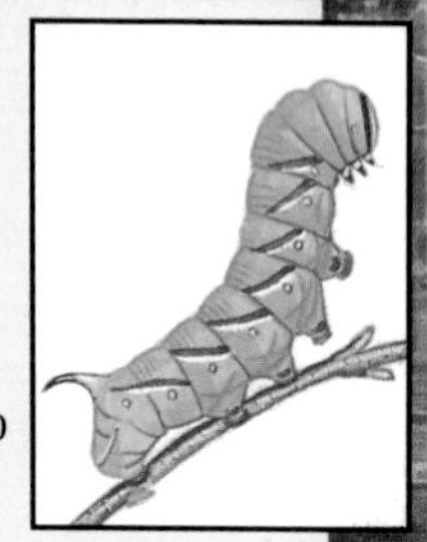

Most plants can only respond slowly to changes. Some turn to follow the Sun around the sky, for example.

*4. Is a stick insect a plant or an animal?*

*5. Some plants can eat animals. True or false?*

*6. Do you know what the yellow flowered plants above are called?*

*7. Plants always grow away from the Sun. True or false?*

## Can car pollution be reduced?

Car exhaust fumes contain poisonous chemicals which cause air pollution. To reduce this, all new cars that use unleaded fuel can be fitted with a machine called a catalytic converter, which cleans exhaust gases. As exhaust gases flow through the converter, they pass over a surface covered with metal atoms. These make the chemicals in the gas react to make less harmful gases.

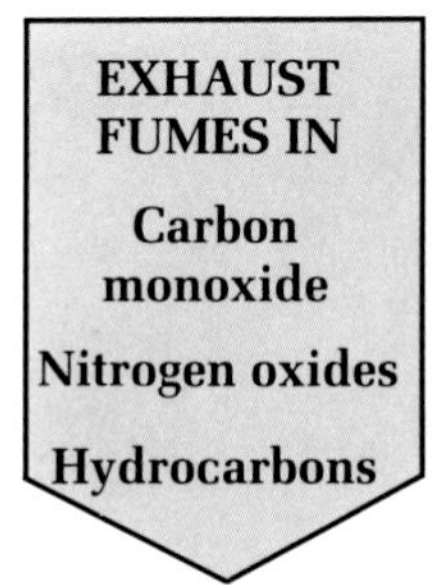


**EXHAUST FUMES OUT**

**Carbon dioxide**

**Nitrogen**

**Water**

**Catalytic converter: palladium, platinum and rhodium atoms.**

*8. How many new cars in the USA are fitted with catalytic converters: a) none; b) half; c) all of them?*

*9. Can exhaust fumes cause acid rain?*

*10. Breathing carbon monoxide makes your hair turn white. True or false?*

## How can light bulbs save energy?

When the metal wire in a light bulb glows, it produces heat as well as light. Producing this heat wastes electrical energy.

**Energy efficient light bulbs**

An energy efficient bulb makes light with chemicals instead of heat. Inside the bulb is a folded fluorescent tube. When electricity passes through it, chemicals glow, giving off light.

*11. Energy efficient light bulbs last: a) 8; b) 30; c) 150 times as long as ordinary bulbs.*

*12. Energy efficient bulbs can only light up in the dark. True or false?*

## How does a camcorder work?

A camcorder is a mini combination of two machines – a TV camera and a video recorder. It works by using lenses to create an image on a tiny light-sensitive electronic component called a charge-coupled device (CCD).

**Electronic circuits send electrical signals to the recording mechanism.**

**Light hits the CCD.**

**Light travels into the camcorder through the lens.**

**You look through the electronic viewfinder.**

**Electrical signals make patterns on the videotape in the recording mechanism.**

*13. What does camcorder stand for?*

**Charge-coupled device (CCD) magnified 1.85 times.**

The CCD is divided into a grid of tiny squares, called pixels, which are coated with a light-sensitive chemical. When light hits the CCD, it generates an electrical signal, which corresponds to the amount of light hitting it. Bright light produces a strong signal and dim light produces a weak signal.

These electrical signals travel to the recording mechanism. Here, the electrical signals create a magnetic field* which makes a pattern on magnetic particles on the surface of a plastic videotape.

The patterns on the tape store the picture information represented by the electrical signals. The sound is recorded on a separate area of the videotape. The tape can then be played back through the camcorder itself or through a video recorder.

**Cutaway of video cassette, to show tape inside.**

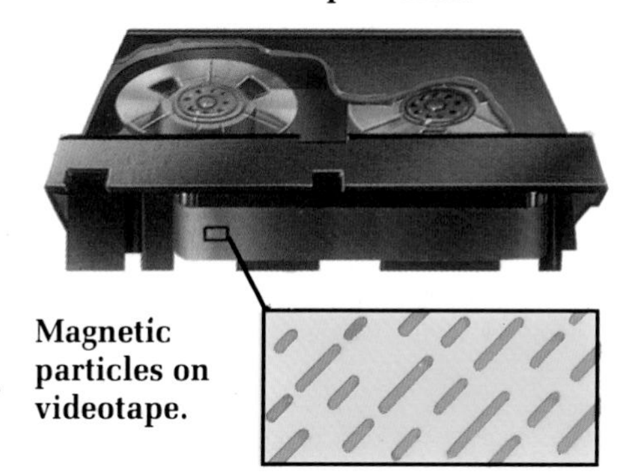

**Magnetic particles on videotape.**

*14. There are about 400,000 pixels on the CCD. True or false?*

*15. What is a palmcorder?*

*See pages 12-13 for more about electricity and magnetism.

# Megaquiz

These ten quizzes test you on what you have read in this book and also on your general knowledge of science.

You can write your answers on a piece of paper and then check on page 32 to see how many you got right.

## Misfits

In each set of three below, there is one misfit. Can you spot which it is?

| 1. | 2. | 3. | 4. | 5. | 6. | 7. | 8. | 9. | 10. |
|---|---|---|---|---|---|---|---|---|---|
| pupil<br>iris<br>pinna | kinetic<br>original<br>chemical | gravity<br>friction<br>density | violet<br>brown<br>indigo | light bulb<br>turbine<br>generator | growth<br>feeding<br>magnetism | cat<br>greyhound<br>mammoth | proton<br>electron<br>siphon | egg<br>baby<br>sperm | flute<br>xylophone<br>drum |

## Inventions and discoveries

Can you match these inventions and discoveries to their dates?

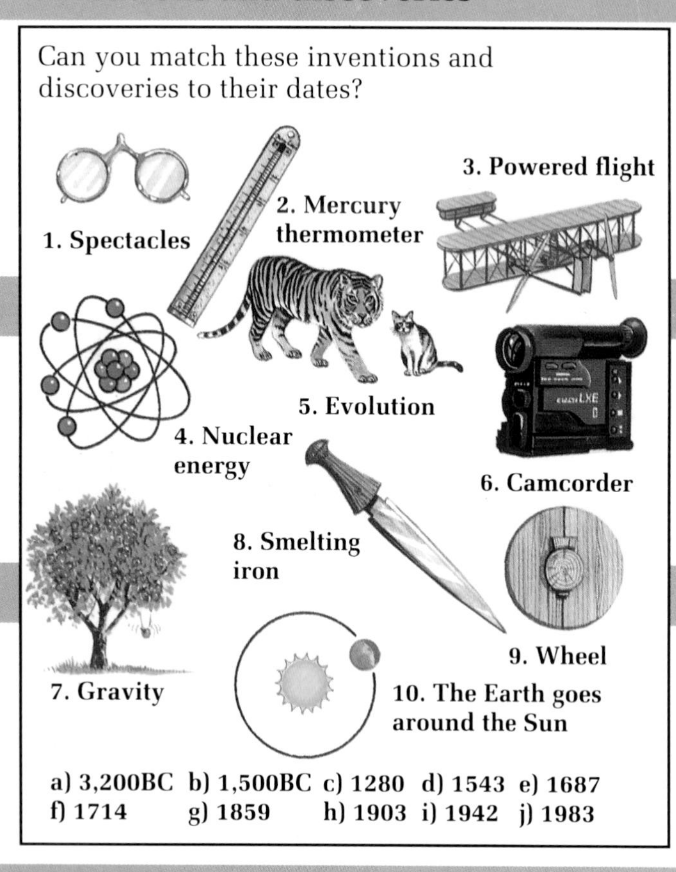


a) 3,200BC b) 1,500BC c) 1280 d) 1543 e) 1687
f) 1714 g) 1859 h) 1903 i) 1942 j) 1983

## Talking science

Each of these sentences is missing a word. The missing words are highlighted in the box below. Can you match the words and sentences?

1. At ....., the sky may appear orange and red.
2. Rotting fruit and vegetables can be used to make.....
3. Gold, silicon and oxygen are all ......
4. The Earth is surrounded by its own magnetic ....., with a north and a south pole.
5. A ..... splits light into the different colours of the rainbow.
6. All animals and plants in an environment are linked to each other by a ..... web.
7. ..... is the force which pulls you to the ground.
8. Our solar system is part of a ..... called the Milky Way.
9. Acid rain causes ..... in many places, including lakes, forests and cities.
10. Plastic is a good ..... of electricity.

| food | prism | compost |
|---|---|---|

| sunset | field | galaxy | insulator |
|---|---|---|---|

| gravity | elements | pollution |
|---|---|---|

## Materials

1. Which material is the best conductor of electricity: a) air; b) wood; c) metal?
2. Name one harmful substance that may be found in car exhaust fumes.
3. Which raw material is different from the others: a) ore; b) coal; c) trees; d) clay?
4. Is water a compound or an element?
5. Where does suede come from?
6. In the past, what precious metal did alchemists try to make?
7. Which gas is the Sun made out of?
8. The cells of living things contain which material: a) oil; b) water; c) blood?
9. Which metal is used in electrical wiring?
10. Which of these raw materials is not used to make energy: a) cocoa; b) coal; c) clay; d) oil?

## Close-ups

These are all close-ups of pictures in the book. Can you recognize what they are?

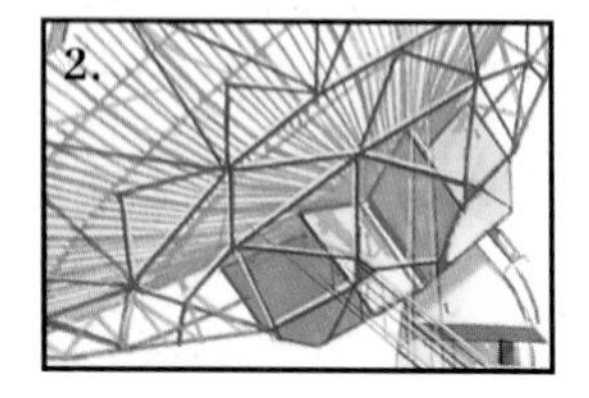


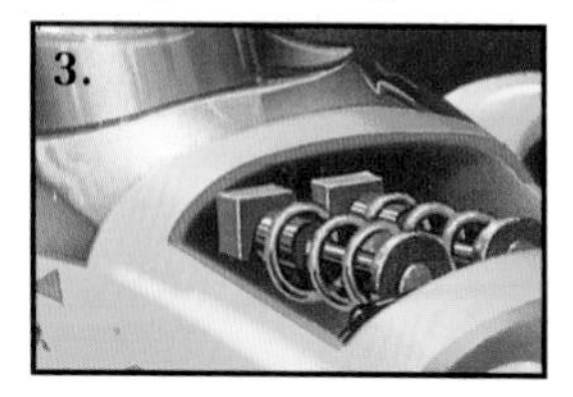

## Animals and plants

Which of these living things...

1. ...do thrushes eat?
2. ...is the loudest animal in the world?
3. ...reflects all the colours in sunlight?
4. ...comes from a horse chestnut tree?
5. ...uses echoes to find insects to eat?
6. ...is extinct?
7. ...was bred to herd animals?
8. ...is the nearest animal relative to a chimpanzee and a gorilla?
9. ...eats sand eels?
10. ...lives in a warren?

## True or false?

1. When you look at the stars you are looking back in time.
2. Green plants scare caterpillars away.
3. All metals are magnetic.
4. Daylight is a mixture of colours.
5. Two-thirds of your body is water.
6. Stomach cells have teeth.
7. Tiny particles exist which are smaller than an atom.
8. Telephones are connected by cables containing bundles of string.
9. Foxes are herbivores.
10. Sound travels in waves.

## Silhouettes

All these silhouettes are things that appear in the book. How many can you recognize?

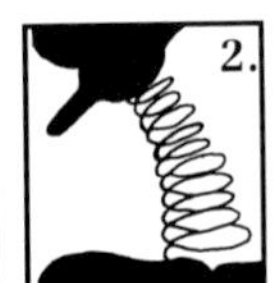

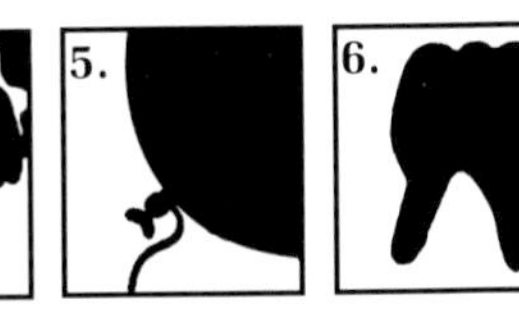

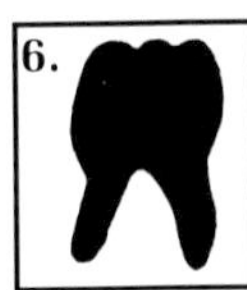

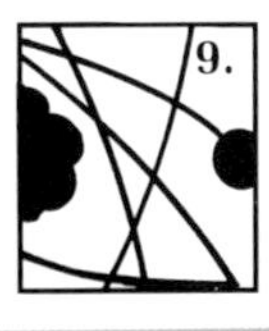

## Body bits

Which part or parts of your body...

1. ...carries oxygen around your body?
2. ...do you no longer need to digest food?
3. ...produces chemicals which control how much you grow?
4. ...carries signals from your eye to your brain?
5. ...covers your whole body?
6. ...enables you to move by squeezing tight and relaxing?
7. ...gives your body its shape?
8. ...opens or closes, to let more or less light into your eye when it is bright or dark?
9. ...is all that is left of a tail?
10. ...directs sounds into your eardrum?

## What do you know?

1. By what process do plants make food?
2. What kind of electricity is lightning?
3. What does CD stand for?
4. Is it possible to see atoms?
5. How many millions of years ago did the Big Bang happen: a) 15 thousand; b) fifty; c) five?
6. What are rocks which contain metals called?
7. What force, apart from electricity, makes an electric motor work?
8. Which material is not made from oil: a) polythene; b) silk; c) acrylic; d) nylon?
9. What sort of light could cut through metal?
10. Are animals or plants at the bottom of a food web?

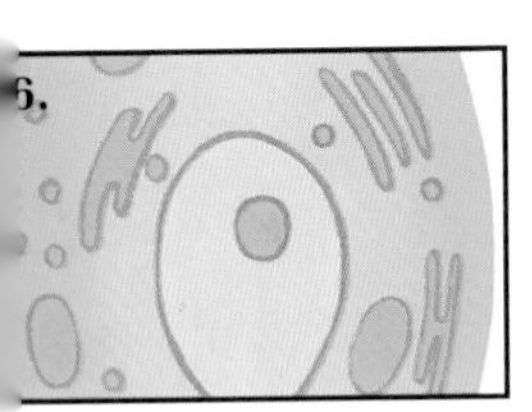

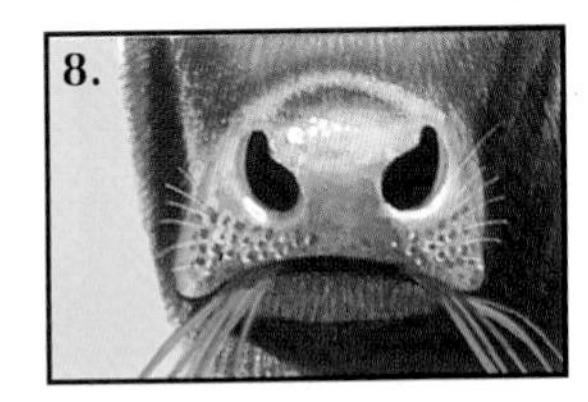

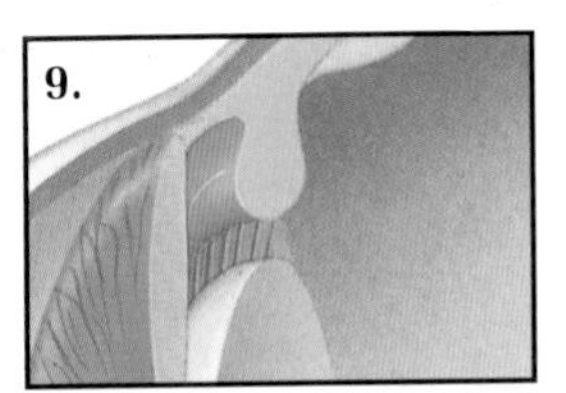

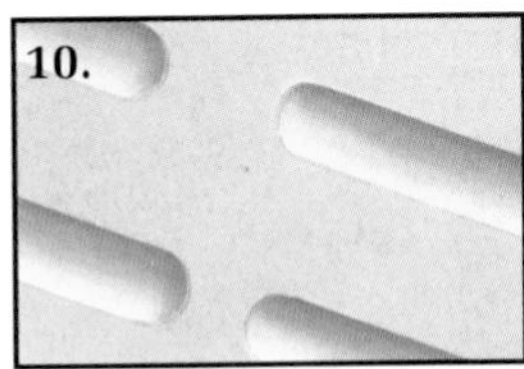

# Quiz answers

**The answers to the 12 quizzes from *Exploring space* to *Science and technology* are on the next four pages. Give yourself one point for every right answer. The chart below helps you to find out how well you have done.**

| | | | |
|---|---|---|---|
| 0-5 | Read through the answers, then try the quiz again. See how many answers you can remember this time. | 11-14 | Good score. If you get this score on most of the quizzes, you have done very well. |
| 6-10 | Quite good. Think more carefully about the questions and you might get more right. | 15 | Excellent. If you do this well in more than half of the quizzes, you are a science genius! |

## Your score overall

You can find out your average score over all 12 quizzes like this:

1. Add up your scores on all 12 quizzes.
2. Divide this total by 12. This is your average score. How well did you do?

## General knowledge

All the answers to general knowledge questions are marked ★. These questions are probably the hardest in the quizzes. Add up how many of them you got right across all 12 quizzes. There are 50 of them in total. If you got over 30 right, your science general knowledge is good.

### Exploring space

1. a) Venus, Neptune and Mars are named after Roman gods.
★ 2. Sirius, Betelgeuse and Alpha Centauri are stars.
3. a) Radio waves from stars contain blips, bleeps and hisses.
4. False. Telescopes were first used around 1600, by scientists such as Galileo.

Galileo used a telescope to help him draw pictures of the Moon.

5. False. X-rays and ultra-violet rays are invisible.
6. c) A group of stars is called a constellation.
7. True. Scientists believe that in 5,000 million years time, the Sun will use up all its fuel and stop shining.
★ 8. No. It is not safe because the Sun is too bright and may hurt your eyes.
9. b) You would find a white dwarf in space. When the fuel in a star is used up, it shrinks and becomes a very dense, planet-like mass, called a white dwarf.
10. b) Apollo 11 landed the first men on the Moon in 1969.
11. True. Dogs were sent up into space on experimental space flights.
12. True. Many ships carry equipment that uses information from satellites to tell them exactly where they are.
13. a) The word "satellite" comes from the Latin word for attendant.
★ 14. The former Soviet Union launched the first satellite in 1957.

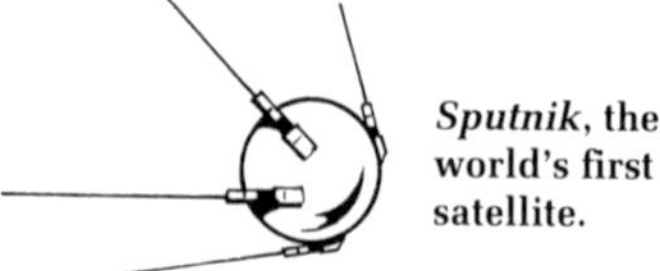
*Sputnik*, the world's first satellite.

15. b) Yuri Gagarin was the first man to go into space, in April 1961.

### What are things made of?

★ 1. Mercury used to be called quicksilver. It is a silvery metal, but it is a liquid at room temperature.
2. True. Diamonds and coal are both made from carbon atoms. The carbon atoms fit together in different ways.

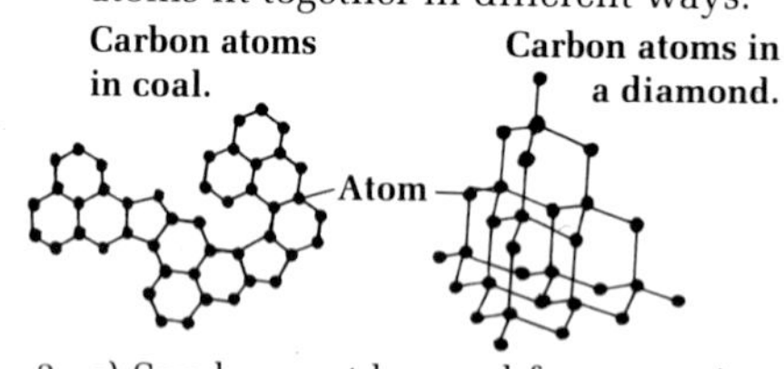


3. c) Sand cannot be used for seasoning food.
★ 4. Water is always ice at the North and South Poles, where the temperature never rises above freezing point.
5. False. Ice forms in many shapes.
★ 6. Yes. Iron is a metal which can be turned into a liquid by heating it.
7. c) When gas is squashed into a smaller space it is called compressed.
8. b) Electrons carry an electrical charge. A flow of electrons is called electricity.
9. a) Power stations use the element uranium to make nuclear energy.
★ 10. Japan. The USA dropped two nuclear bombs there in 1945.
11. c) A microscope which uses lenses to magnify an object is called an optical microscope.

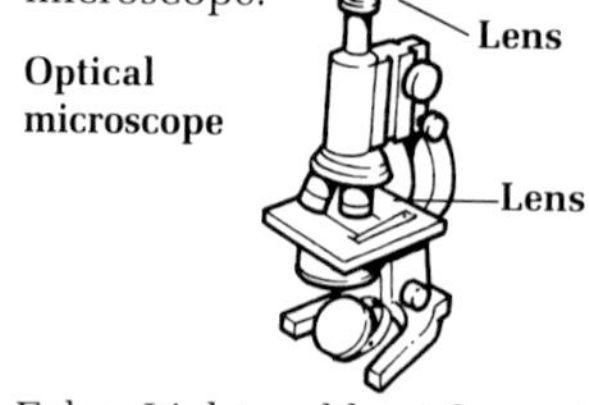


12. False. Light and heat from stars is released by nuclear energy.
★ 13. Smells are gases. Smells spread because gas molecules move easily.
★ 14. Divers, astronauts and fire fighters carry compressed oxygen in tanks.
15. The three elements are gold, copper and oxygen.

### Using materials

★ 1. Oil and fuel; iron ore and bridge; tree and book; clay and crockery; wool and sweater; cocoa and chocolate. Score a point if you got them all right.
2. c) Nylon is a man-made material.
3. a) Texas, USA is famous for crude oil.



★ 4. No. Cooking oil comes from vegetables.
★ 5. The racing car needs to be light in weight to help it travel faster.
★ 6. Rubber comes from latex – the sap of a rubber tree. Score a point if you guessed it was a plant or a tree.

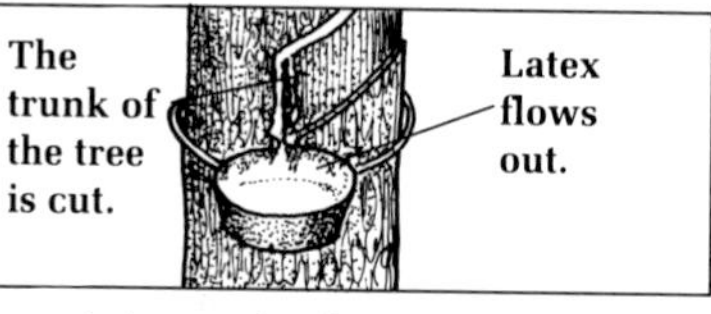


★ 7. The suit has to be fire-resistant to protect the driver if the car crashes, and oil and fuel catch fire.
8. No. Crude oil cannot be used in cars as fuel. It has to be refined first.
9. b) People first made alloys in the Bronze Age. Bronze is an alloy of the metals copper and tin.
10. True. More than three-quarters of all elements are metals.
11. c) This is called a blast furnace. Air is blasted, or blown, into it.
12. True. Many metals react, or change, if they come into contact with air or water. Some metals, such as sodium or potassium, may even explode. For this reason, they are stored in oil.
13. c) The purity of gold is measured in carats. A carat is the amount of pure gold mixed with other metals in an object. 24 carat gold is pure gold.
14. False.
15. a) A thin sheet of gold is called gold leaf. It can be used to cover cheaper metals.

## Moving, flying and floating

1. True. Friction does not act in space, and the weak gravity between the Earth and Moon has very little effect on a fast moving spaceship.
★ 2. Yes. Stone is more dense than chocolate. The material in it is packed closer together.
3. False. Steel is made from iron and carbon. Over 90% of metal produced is either iron or steel.
★ 4. Cyclists crouch low so that air flows over them smoothly, enabling them to go faster.
5. a) A tandem is a bike for two riders.

★ 6. You feel more friction on gravel. Ice has a very smooth surface, so things slide over it, rather than grip it.
7. c) Sliding down a rope might give you a friction burn.
8. True. Most birds have hollow bones to make them lighter. This makes it easier for them to take off and fly.

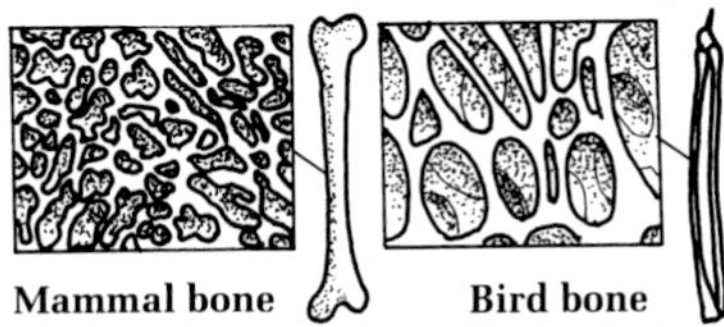


9. b) The first people to fly used aircraft driven by propellers.
★ 10. No. Helicopters have blades. These lift the aircraft into the air directly, making a wing unnecessary.

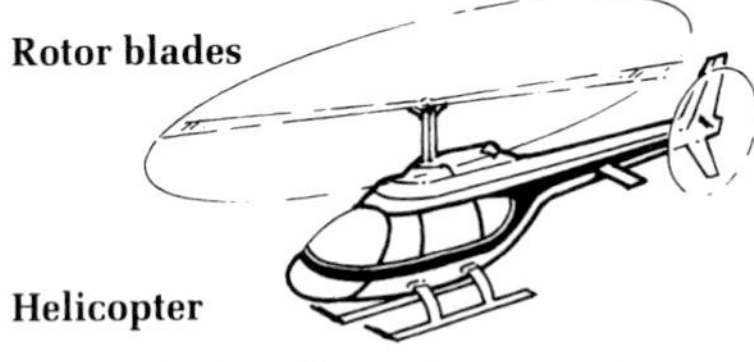


11. True. Gliders fly without engines. They are made with light materials, and glide in patches of warm air.
12. An empty ship would sit higher in the sea. A heavy cargo pushes the ship's hull farther down against the upthrust of the water underneath it.
★ 13. Cork floats. It is less dense than water.
14. c) A submarine dives by filling compartments, called ballast tanks, with water. This makes it heavier than water so it sinks. It surfaces by filling these tanks with a supply of compressed air.

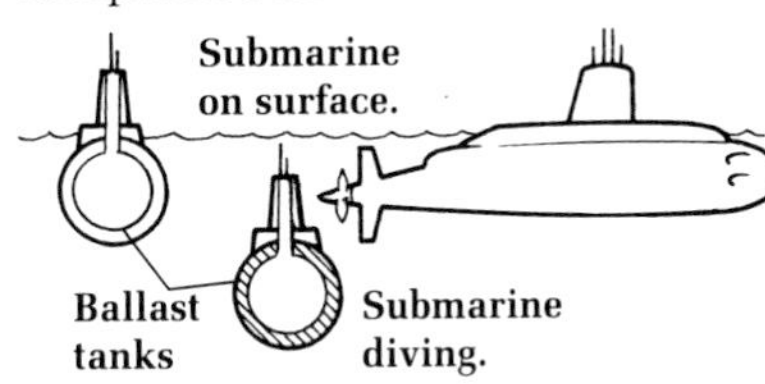


15. b) Isaac Newton was well known for studying mathematics.

## Making things work

1. A piece of stretched elastic has potential energy, which will be released when the elastic is let go.

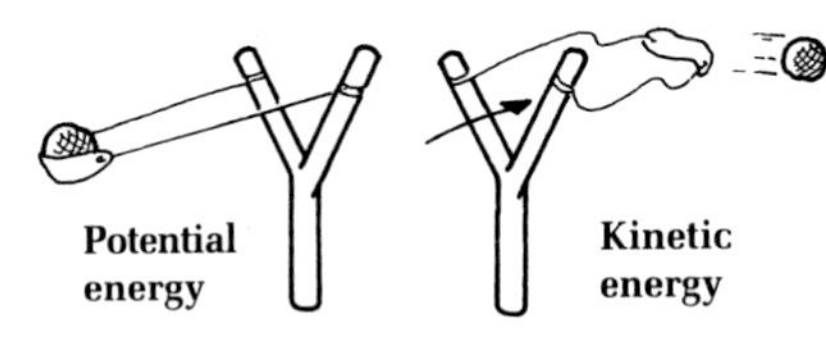


2. False. Steam has more energy than hot water, because it is hotter and its molecules are moving faster.
★ 3. You would find the following forms of energy in lightning: heat, light, electrical and kinetic. Score a point if you got two or more.
4. b) The first nuclear power station opened in 1956.
5. Yes. Sound can travel through walls.
6. True. Animal manure can be used to produce energy. When it rots it gives off a gas called methane, or biogas. Millions of people in China already use this gas as a fuel.

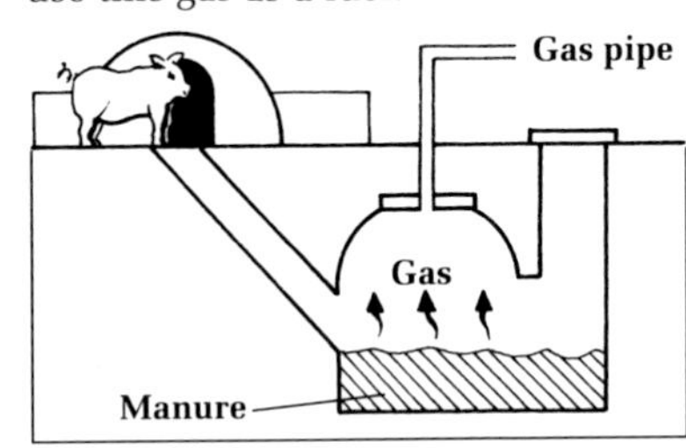


7. b) Oil, coal and natural gas are called fossil fuels.
8. True. The Sun evaporates water from the Earth's surface. The water then condenses to form clouds and falls as rain. This cycle of water would not be possible without heat from the Sun.
9. a) Uranium is a type of metal.
★ 10. A burning candle produces heat and light energy.
11. c) Sound cannot travel through space because there are no air particles to pass on sound waves.
12. True. Most energy produced by a light bulb is heat.
13. a) Energy in food is measured in Calories.

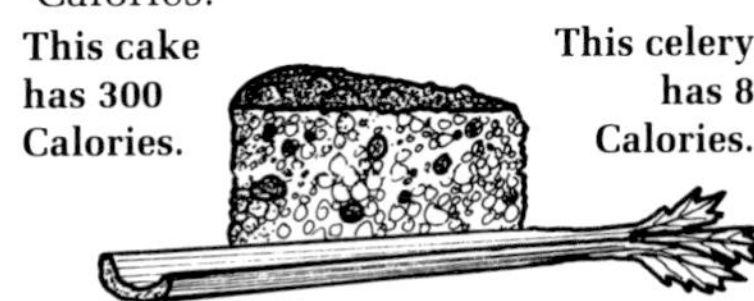


14. A fat person has more stored energy than a thin person. If you eat more food than your body uses for energy, the extra is stored in your body as fat.
★ 15. Yes. Even when you are asleep, your body still uses energy.

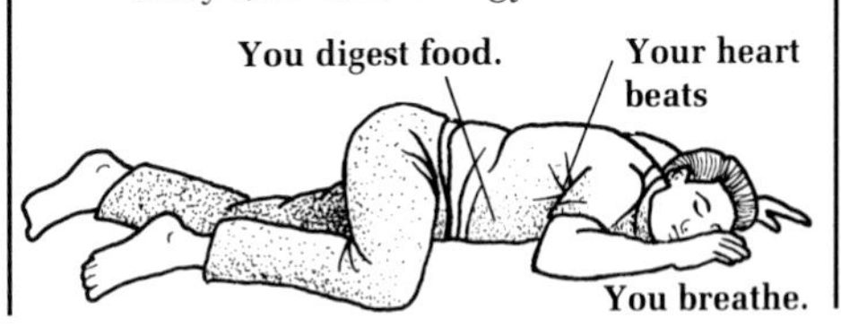


## Electricity and magnetism

1. No. Brass, like all metals, is a conductor of electricity.
★ 2. No. Some turbines are turned by running water, for example in hydroelectric power stations. The wind can also work turbines.

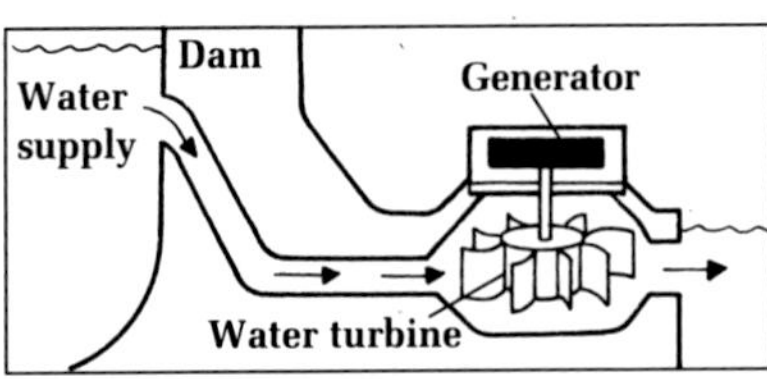


3. False. Thunder is caused by lightning heating up the air it passes through. The air expands rapidly, creating a bang.
★ 4. Lightning always hits the highest point on the ground beneath it. This is why tall buildings have lightning rods to draw the lightning to them, rather than the building they are on.
5. a) Hair standing on end can be caused by static electricity.
6. False. There is nothing to stop lightning from striking the same place, such as a lightning rod, twice.
7. True. Your heart makes tiny electric shocks to keep it beating. These shocks can be measured by a machine called an electrocardiograph.

**Electrocardiographs record your heartbeat in a pattern like this.**

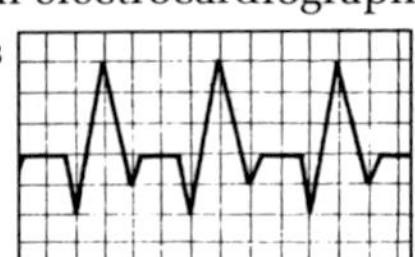

8. a) Rubber boots. Rubber is a very good insulator. If you were to touch a live electric wire while wearing rubber boots, the rubber would prevent the electricity from flowing through you and reaching the ground.
★ 9. It is unsafe because water could seep into the appliance and conduct electricity to your body. This could give you a dangerous electric shock.
★ 10. No. Wood is not a magnetic material.
★ 11. Yes. The Earth has a metal core, which has a magnetic field. This makes the magnetic material in a compass needle point north.

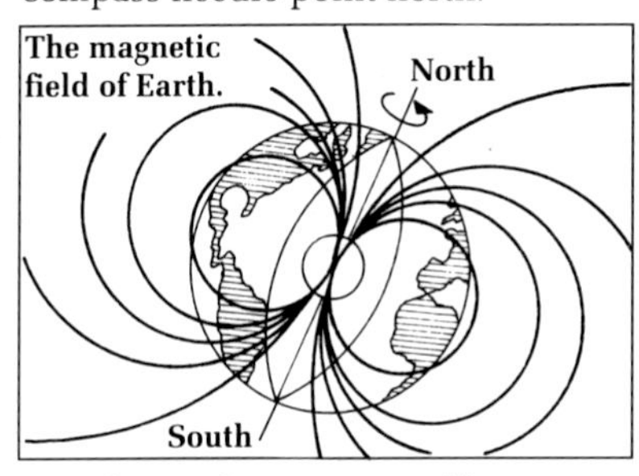


**The magnetic field of Earth.**

12. No. Glue picks up material because it is sticky. It has no magnetic quality.
13. c) Watts are units of electrical power.
14. d) A washing machine uses an electric motor.
★ 15. c) The electric motor was invented in England, in 1821, by Michael Faraday.

## Sound and music

1. A clap of thunder is louder than a handclap, so it has more energy.
2. c) The loudness of sound is measured in decibels (or dB).
3. ★ Yes. Sound travels around corners. Sound waves spread out as they go through gaps or around obstacles.
4. False. The bones in the middle ear are called the hammer, anvil and stirrup.

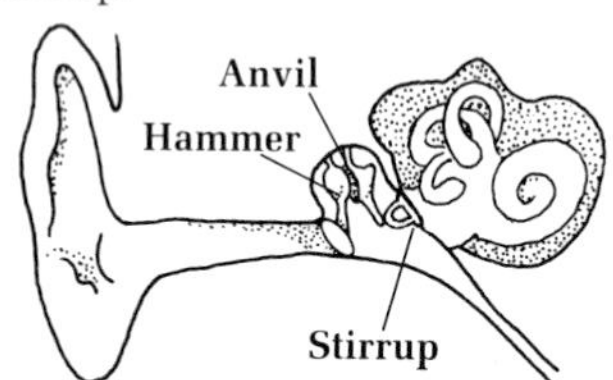


5. a) Balance. Inside your ear are three semi-circular tubes. These contain liquid which flows against tiny hair cells when you move. These cells send signals to your brain telling you which way you have moved.
6. True. Fish pick up sound vibrations with a tube-like organ called the lateral line, which runs along their bodies.

7. ★ Yes. Children can hear higher frequencies than adults.
8. ★ You would hear an echo better on a calm day. On a windy day, returning sound waves would be scattered.
9. False. However, some sounds can travel a very long way, especially in water. Underwater loudspeakers can make sounds in the Antarctic, that scientists can detect in the Arctic.

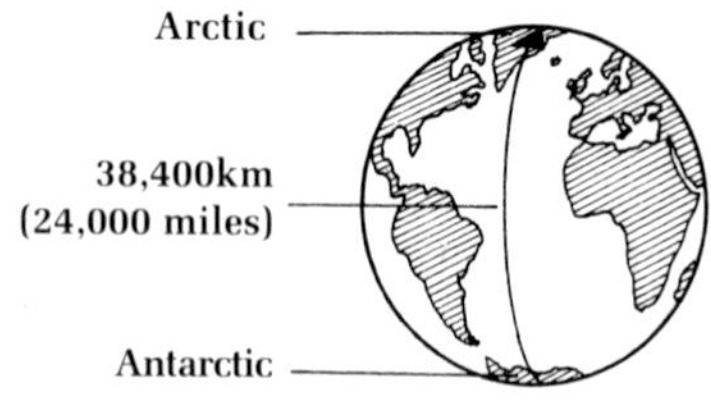


10. b) Locating objects by listening to high frequency echoes is called sonar. It stands for SOund, NAvigation and Ranging.
11. False.
12. True. The sound humpback whales make has specific notes and patterns which they repeat, like a bird's song.
13. a) Drums, cymbals and xylophones are all percussion instruments. This type of instrument is struck to make sounds.
14. Angor, batu, napio and tirgua can be unscrambled to make these instruments.

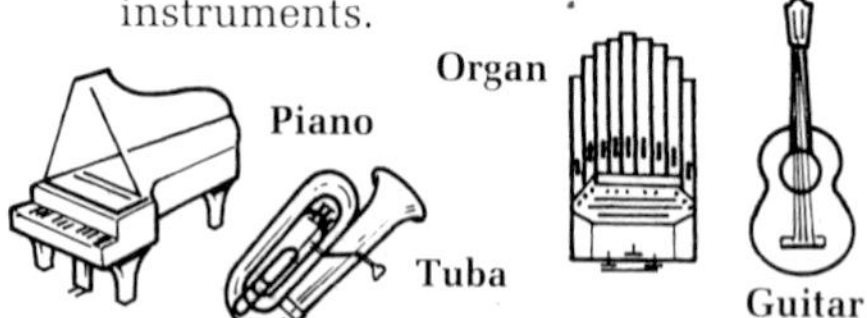


15. c) A place without any air is called a vacuum.

## Light and colour

1. c) Red and yellow make orange.
2. b) Another name for the colours of the rainbow is a spectrum.
3. No. Light travels in straight lines. Light can only go around a corner if it is reflected off a surface.

4. False. Most animals have colour vision, but some, such as dogs, can only see in black and white.
5. True. Fireflies and some sea animals make light with chemicals produced inside them. They make light to attract a mate or to lure food.

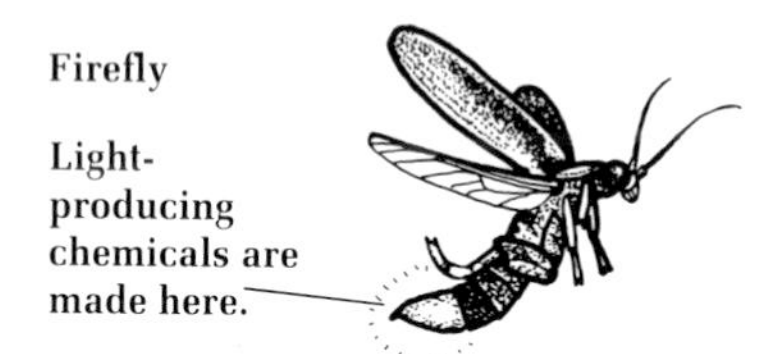


6. Snow reflects all the colours in white light equally well.
7. c) The sea is blue because it reflects the sky, which is also blue.
8. ★ Yes. Light can travel through space. If it could not, we would have no sunlight on Earth.
9. True. Ancient Egyptians made mirrors from polished bronze metal.

10. ★ Yes. Polished wood is fairly smooth. Some light is reflected evenly off this smooth surface, so you see a reflection.
11. False. The eye is filled with fluid. This helps bend light towards the retina.

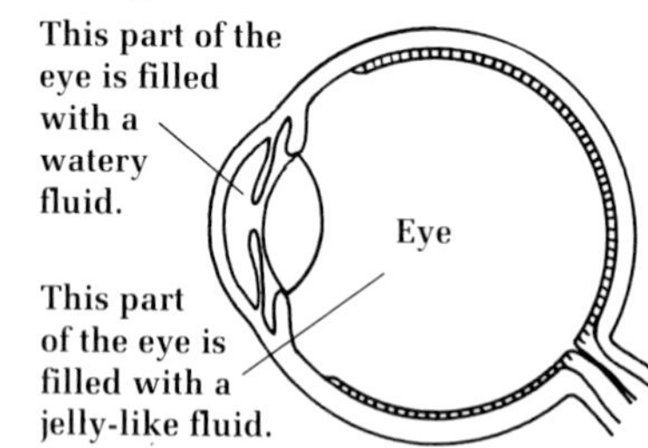


12. ★ You need to blink in order to clean the surface of the eye.
13. a) This part of the eye is called the cornea. Along with the lens and eye fluids, it focuses light on the retina.
14. b) Cats and c) owls can see well in the dark. They hunt at night because there is less competition for food.
15. ★ Lightning travels faster than thunder. Thunder and lightning happen at the same time, but lightning reaches you first because light travels faster than sound.

## Living things

1. c) Plants do not think. However, some can react very quickly. For example, when you touch a mimosa plant, its leaves collapse. This may shake off insects that are trying to eat it.
2. False. An erupting volcano is no more alive than the wind and the rain.
3. b) This animal is an orang-utan.
4. ★ A stick insect is an animal. It looks like a twig.

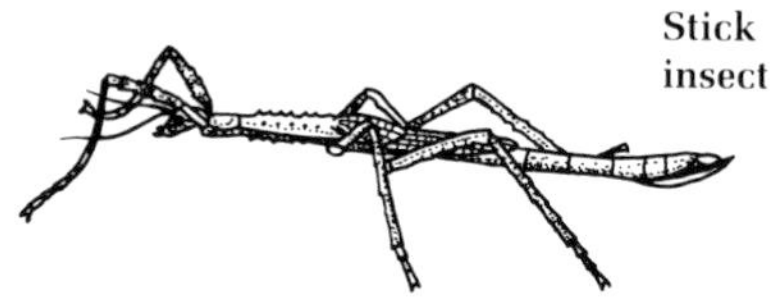


5. True. There are several plants, such as the venus flytrap, which catch and eat insects and other small animals.

6. ★ These plants are called sunflowers.
7. False. Plants grow towards sunlight to absorb as much energy as possible.
8. c) The pancreas is not a bone. It is a group of cells, called a gland, which produces digestive juices.

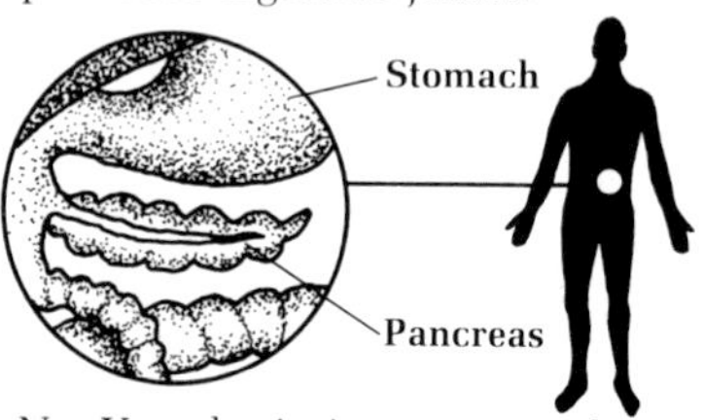


9. ★ No. Your brain is not a muscle. It is an organ. An organ is a specific part of the body, such as the heart or the liver, which does a particular job.
10. a) In the womb, a baby is attached to the mother by the umbilical cord, which suppplies it with food and oxygen.

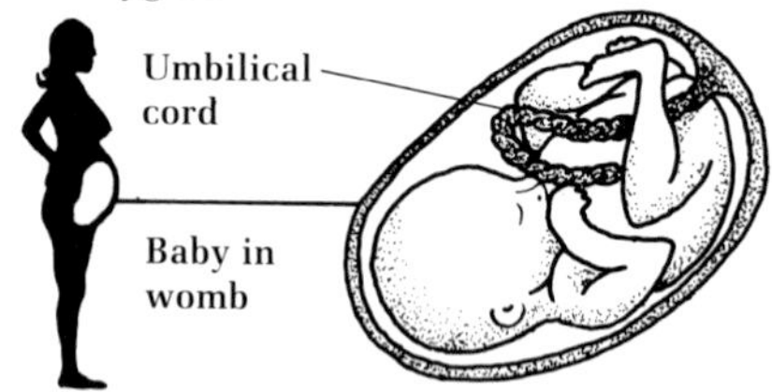


11. An egg cell is much bigger than a sperm cell.
12. c) Protein, found in meat, cheese and fish, is essential for growth.
13. True. When you get up in the morning, you are at full height. During the day, gravity presses down on you and closes the tiny gaps between your joints. By the evening you are a little shorter.
14. True. There are 206 bones in your body, including 32 in each arm and 31 in each leg.
15. a) Your nails never stop growing while you are alive.

## Evolution

1. False. Scientists think that domestic cats have evolved from wild cats, possibly from Africa.
2. ★ No. You should not eat horse chestnut seeds, but you can bake and eat the seeds of sweet chestnut trees.

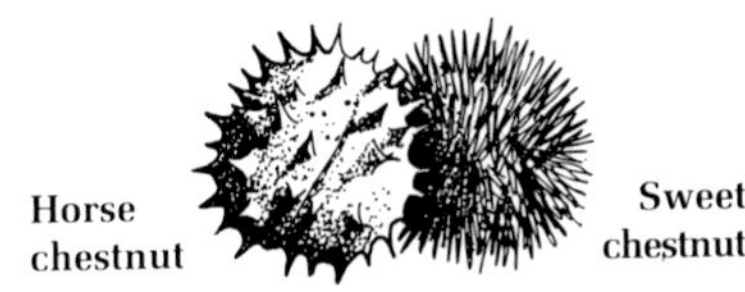


3. Yes. Animals with short life-spans and many offspring evolve quicker, because any change in their appearance or the way they act will be passed on to their own offspring much quicker.
4. ★ Moths usually come out at night.
5. False.
6. b) The armadillo is not extinct. Armadillos are found in North and South America, and have thick bony plates around their bodies to protect them from predators.

7. ★ Present day tigers have stripes to help them blend in with the light and shade of the forests they inhabit.

Modern tiger

Sabre-tooth tiger

8. No. Wisdom teeth are found in all sorts of people.
9. a) Eyebrows help to keep sweat from the brow out of the eyes.
10. b) Most scientists think the first humans lived in Africa.
11. a) Pedigree dogs. A dog must have ancestors of the same breed for three generations (back to its great grandparents), to be a pedigree dog.
12. c) The husky is most like a wolf.

13. No. Lions are the product of natural selection in the wild. They are too fierce and dangerous to be of any practical use to humans.
14. ★ The mule is a cross between a donkey and a horse. Mules are strong animals, but they cannot usually have their own offspring.
15. c) Genetic engineering is a branch of biotechnology.

## The balance of nature

1. False. The study of living things in the environment is called ecology.
2. b) Protecting the environment is called conservation.
3. ★ Hawks hunt by day, when they make the best use of their sharp eyesight.

Sparrowhawks hide in trees and ambush their prey.

4. The thrush has more choice of food than the owl. It is an omnivore, eating both plants and animals.
5. In this particular food web, rabbits need to watch out for foxes.
6. False. Many large animals, such as elephants and horses, are herbivores.
7. ★ Humans are omnivores.
8. There would be more caterpillars than hawks in a forest food web. For a food web to feed all its animals, there have to be more animals at the lower end to provide food for those at the top.
9. b) The boring beetle is a real beetle.

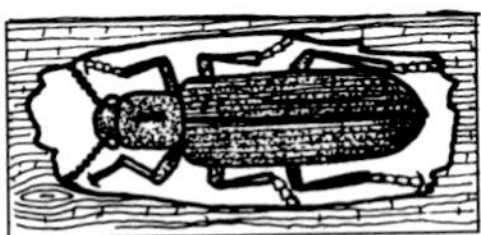
Boring beetles burrow into trees.

10. a) Sites where waste is buried are called landfills.
11. ★ Chernobyl power station caused much pollution when it exploded in 1986. Large parts of the former Soviet Union and Northern Europe were affected.

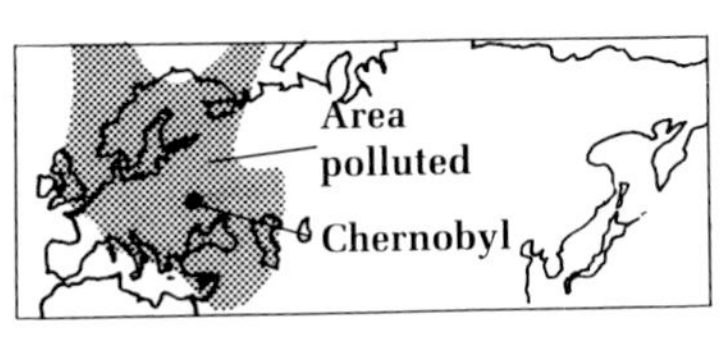


12. ★ Yes. Almost half the iron used to make steel is recycled. Recycling iron is cheaper, and uses less energy than making new iron from iron ore.
13. c) Compost heaps take around six months to rot.
14. b) Materials that rot are called biodegradable, which means they can be broken down by bacteria. Materials made from living things are able to rot, but metals, glass and most plastics do not rot.

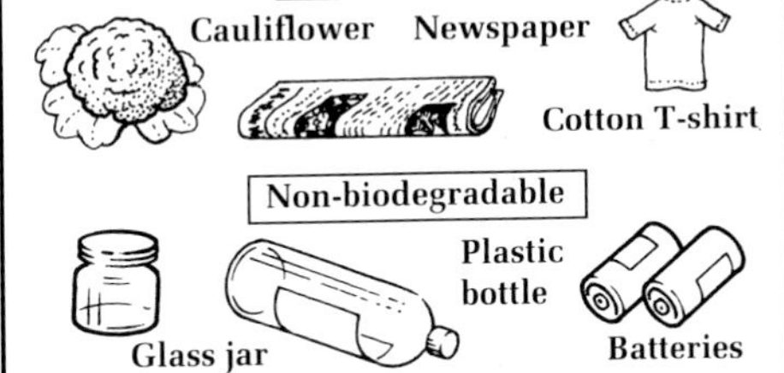


15. True. In 1990, Americans threw away nearly 2kg (4lbs) of waste a day.

## Science and technology

1. b) CDs are coated with a protective layer of transparent plastic.
2. ★ No. Written information and pictures can also be stored on CD.
3. c) The picture has been magnified around 8,000 times.
4. False. CDs are very hard-wearing. It is unlikely that they will wear out. Unlike records and tapes which rub against another hard surface, the CD surface is only touched by light.
5. True. Lasers are used to read bar codes. The reflections of the laser beam form a digital code, which registers the price of goods.

6. ★ Yes. Laser light travels in a straight line and is used to measure distances.

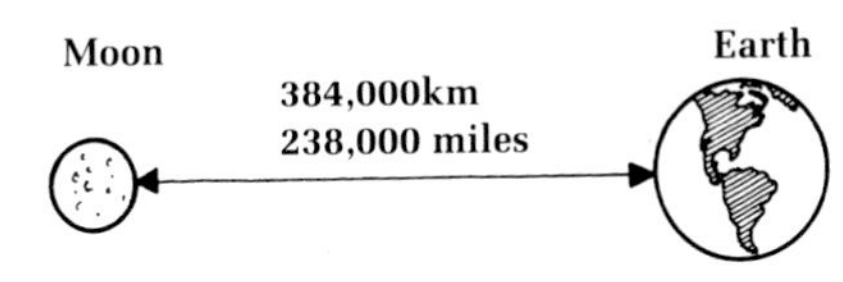

Lasers have measured the distance between the Earth and the Moon.

7. True. Some lasers are brighter than the Sun. Scientists are trying to find a way to use bright lasers to generate nuclear power.
8. c) All new cars in the USA are fitted with catalytic converters.
9. ★ Yes. Exhaust fumes are acidic. They dissolve in moisture in the air, which then falls as acid rain.

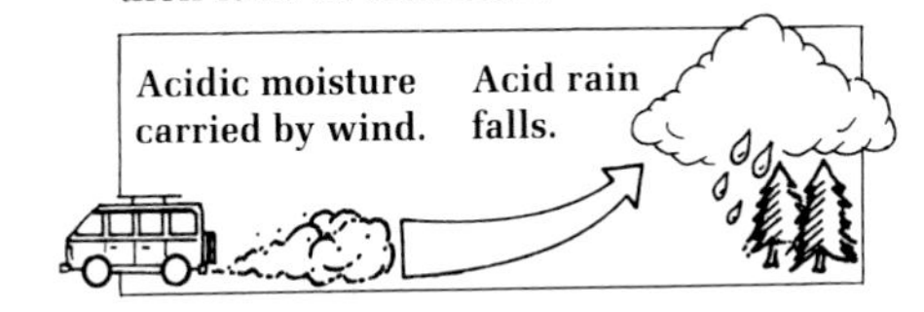


10. False. Breathing carbon monoxide will not make your hair go white, but it is poisonous. If you breathe a great deal of it, it can kill you.
11. a) Energy efficient light bulbs last 8 times longer than ordinary bulbs.
12. False. Energy efficient light bulbs work as long as there is an electricity supply.
13. Camcorder stands for CAMera and reCORDER.
14. True. There are about 400,000 pixels on a CCD.
15. ★ A palmcorder is a very small, modern camcorder, named because it can be held in one hand. The lightest ones weigh around 800g (1lb 12oz).

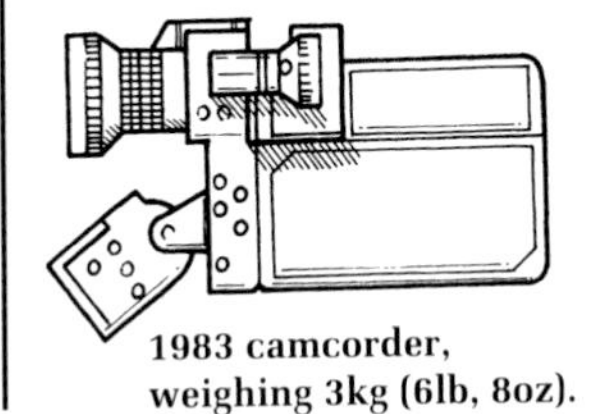
1983 camcorder, weighing 3kg (6lb, 8oz).

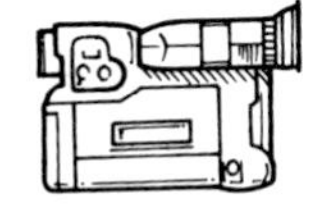
1993 palmcorder.

# Megaquiz answers

**There are 100 possible points in the whole Megaquiz. If you score over 50 you have done well. Over 75 is excellent. You can find out more about some of the answers on the page listed after it.**

### Misfits

1. The pinna is not part of the eye.
2. Original is not a type of energy.
3. Density is not a force.
4. Brown is not a colour of the rainbow.
5. A lightbulb does not make electricity.
6. Magnetism is not a feature of all living things.
7. The mammoth is extinct.
8. A siphon is not part of an atom.
9. A baby is not a cell.
10. Flutes are not percussion instruments.

### Inventions and discoveries

1. Spectacles (c).
2. Mercury thermometer (f).
3. Powered flight (h).
4. Nuclear energy (i).
5. Evolution (g).
6. Camcorder (j).
7. Gravity (e).
8. Smelting iron (b).
9. Wheel (a).
10. The Earth goes around the Sun (d).

### Talking science

1. Sunset (page 16).
2. Compost (page 23).
3. Elements (page 4).
4. Field (page 13).
5. Prism (page 16).
6. Food (page 22).
7. Gravity (page 8).
8. Galaxy (page 2).
9. Pollution (page 25).
10. Insulator (page 12).

### Materials

1. c) metal (page 12).
2. Hydrocarbons/nitrogen/carbon monoxide (page 25).
3. c) trees (pages 6-7).
4. A compound (page 4).
5. Animal skin (page 6).
6. Gold (page 7).
7. Hydrogen (page 2).
8. b) water (page 19).
9. Copper (page 12).
10. c) clay (page 10-11).

### Close-ups

1. Owl (page 22).
2. Radio telescope (page 2).
3. Suspension springs (page 7).
4. Peppered moth (page 20).
5. Camcorder (page 25).
6. Cell (page 18).
7. Atoms (page 4).
8. Cow (page 10).
9. Eye (page 17).
10. Compact disc (page 24).

### Animals and plants

1. (d) berries.
2. (c) blue whale.
3. (a) white cat.
4. (g) horse chestnut seed.
5. (b) bat.
6. (e) sabre-toothed tiger.
7. (i) old English sheepdog.
8. (j) orang-utan.
9. (h) puffin.
10. (f) rabbit.

### True or false?

1. True (page 3).
2. False.
3. False.
4. True (page 16).
5. True (page 19).
6. False.
7. True (page 5).
8. False.
9. False.
10. True (page 14).

### Silhouettes

1. Hawk (page 22).
2. Spring (page 10).
3. Ship (page 9).
4. Coccyx (page 21).
5. Balloon (page 4).
6. Wisdom tooth (page 21).
7. Guitar (page 15).
8. Nerve cell (page 19).
9. Atom (page 5).
10. Caterpillar (page 18).

### Body bits

1. Blood (page 11).
2. Appendix (page 21).
3. Pituitary gland (page 19).
4. Optic nerve (page 17).
5. Skin.
6. Muscles (page 19).
7. Skeleton (page 19).
8. Iris (page 17).
9. Coccyx (page 21).
10. Pinna (page 14).

### What do you know?

1. Photosynthesis (page 18).
2. Static electricity (page 12).
3. Compact disc (page 24).
4. Yes, with an electron microscope.
5. a) 15 thousand (page 2).
6. Ores (page 6).
7. Magnetism (page 13).
8. b) silk (page 6).
9. Laser light (page 24).
10. Plants (page 22).

# Index




The publishers would like to thank the following for the use of their photographs and reference material in this book: NRSC LTD/ Science Photo Library (page 3, left); Dr Mitsuo Ohtsuki/Science Photo Library (page 5, bottom right); Canon (UK) Ltd (page 25, top).

First published in 1993 by Usborne Publishing Ltd, 83-85 Saffron Hill, London, EC1N 8RT, England.







First published in America August 1993





Printed in Spain.